OTTO'S NIGHT WATCH

by
OTTO BOUTIN

The Heritage of the Printer Series

Published by Irvin J. Borowsky

with illustrations

North American Publishing Company
One Hundred Thirty-four North Thirteenth Street
Philadelphia, Pa. 19107

International Standard Book Number 0-912920-03-3
Library of Congress Catalog Card Number 72-85048
PRINTED IN THE UNITED STATES OF AMERICA

ORDER NO. 7206

Contents

Foreword

MARK Twain still lives.

As before he still inspires laughter, dry humor, the sense of the absurd, and above all the warmth of human, compassionate understanding in the heart of every printer. But instead of speaking or writing from beyond the grave the spirit that was Twain the Printer resides in a modest typesetter in Chicago, Illinois who still makes his living pounding the keys of a linotype machine.

Otto Boutin is a real, live printer. Perhaps he is the last one alive who still embodies in his own life story and in his personality the characteristic traits that embodied and personified the American printer from the Civil War days, through the turbulent era when Mergenthaler's contraption turned a craft into a science, and through the 20's when craftmanship in the strong personalized individualized sense made its supreme, final struggle, also to die — perhaps forever — in the depression years.

Yes, there are still printer-craftsmen around. They still exist in the hearts and souls of every man who has set his hands on the keyboard of a linecaster, or tied string around a page that soon pied, or gripped upon the press clutch as printer's ink slithered across his hand. These printer-craftsmen now know that they can exist only in the spirit, but not for long in a world where return-on-investment, cash-flow, and electronics dominate an industry. The printer-craftsman, as epitomized by those wanderers who spend the most vital parts of their lives in the pressroom, cannot long survive in the age of plastics and jet airplanes. They are human beings and printers first, and business men second, if ever.

Therein lies the fascination of Otto and his creations. No, "creations" is a bad word, for while parading as fiction Otto tells the life stories of actual people who have lived and died in the composing room and the pressroom, sometimes with a galley proof clutched in their hands. Today's printer is besieged by business problems everywhere. He is tied down by mortgages, banker's loans, accounts receivable and accounts payable. No one today dares tear off the golden chains he wraps so quickly and desperately around his neck, for who can argue that to succeed in the printing business is the most important thing in life, and that the greatest achievement is to increase sales volume each year?

Yet Otto, with all his printer skills, with all his ability to take apart and put together a linecaster blindfolded, turns his back upon the things we hold most dear. He does not do so as the hippy youngster may do, spurning its value. Rather he asks himself sadly, and the reader too, "is it all worth it?"

While setting type he dreams of faraway places, of sun-kissed shores, and wide open fields. What is most important, he turns those dreams into reality and when the mood moves him he says goodbye to the plant where he has worked. He bids goodbye to profit-sharing plans, to Christmas bonuses, to retirement funds, and goes off somewhere else in search of something — what? The Great Printing Plant Across the Wide Missouri? Who knows? For it is Otto's supreme skill to make the wish to leave, the excuse, the pretense, the explanation, only a symbol for whatever personal reasons the reader may have for yearning to chuck the whole business and start anew somewhere — just doing a job. Now and then Otto, and all of us, may think of expanding, of growing, of getting into the Big Time, but his heart is not really there. All that he holds really dear is his skill as a printer — and that is something he can take with him anywhere. Somewhere, somehow, he can always find some sympathetic soul who could put his talents to practical use.

With Otto, constantly in the background, is The Woman. But she is not a woman as most of us know her. Or rather, Otto sees her as part of every man sees her. Despite her outward appearance, whether she be beautiful or comical, rich, or talented, and despite whatever her wiles and attractions may be, she is to Otto and to every man, a source of suspicion and possible danger. Woman, to Otto, represents precisely the thing which total commitment to the Printing Plant means. And that is bondage and loss of freedom.
that is bondage and loss of freedom.

A woman, like the management or ownership of a plant, can tie a man down. How can a man dream, and just pack up his troubles in his old kit bag and go, go, go, if there is a Woman, or a Printing Plant to tie one down?

Otto's story, then, is essentially the story of every man's search for freedom. But it is told in terms which are readily recognized by anyone who has worked in a printing plant. It is told in anecdotes about printers, printing plants, and printing operations. It is told mostly about a class of printers, Tramp Printers they were called, who knew nothing of union rules and regulations, or management's prerogatives. They knew only their own worth as craftsmen, and their own worth as human beings. They knew true freedom, and when it was threatened, they left, despite the cost to them in time and effort. The Tramp Printers, in Otto's stories, though he never uses the word since he and his people reject classification and insist on being individuals, are gone. A few remain in our memory. Most remain in our hearts as symbols of the truth that Otto tells about our inner thoughts, our inner feelings, as we go about daily work as Craftsmen.

The stories published herein have all appeared in Printing Impressions and continue to do so. They have never been published in any hard-bound book. As one of the most popular feature writers for Printing Impressions, Otto Boutin has been the recipient of many honors and awards for his perceptive, moving accounts of his fellow printers with whom he has worked, and with whom he continues to work.

At this moment Otto is watching the matrices slide down, and soon another hot slug will drop. As his fingertips touch the keyboard, they also touch the keys to our inner being, our heart.

The Editors of Printing Impressions

Love Letter to an Old Linotype

L OVE Letter to an Old Linotype:
  I felt sorry for you the other day when the efficiency experts decided you were too old to keep on working.

I did my best to show that you still could produce six slugs a minute, even with an old duffer like me at the keyboard. But that's not enough for the wonder boys. They want to run tape through everything, but not through an old Model Five like you.

And they said I'm too old for this tape operation, same as you are. Maybe they're right. I don't want a tape running through my head, in one ear and out the other. I'd rather go back to selling peanuts in the ball park.

It's tough to see you go, you old clonker. We've done a lot of living together. The first time I met you I was as nervous as a

1

bashful boy on his first date. I tried hard to please you, but kept doing everything wrong. And I kept stuttering, especially in the caps. I never wanted to see you again. But I came back.

Eventually I got to like you. You were quite a gal that time, all shined up and full of ideals. You had just been through a war to end all wars, the one that made the world safe for democracy. It was while sitting with you in the evenings that I learned a lot of names like Georges Clemenceau, Tomas Masaryk and Lloyd George.

As the years went by we had conversations together every night. You told me about the German inflation, about Cal Coolidge being sworn in as President, and about Lindy landing in Paris. That was some story, wasn't it? A kid from Minnesota flying across the ocean all alone. We pounded out column after column after column of that story, night after night, and we loved it. That was a happy story.

We were hot shots that time. Visitors used to watch you work, remarking that you were almost human— and that I was almost a machine. We got along together real good.

And then something happened in Wall Street and I found myself out in the cold. There were a dozen men anxious to spend the evening with you. Now and then you favored me, but not too often.

You really can't blame me if I began to parade outside your window with signs hanging over my shoulders telling the world that you were taking unfair advantage of me. You felt so humiliated that you froze up for a month, refusing to have anything to do with anyone.

When we got back together we had to learn a lot of new names. Haile Selassi, Mussolini, Franco, Von Ribbentrop, Goebbels, Goering, Hitler. Our conversations had lost their cheerfulness. Then we separated for a while, because there were other things for me to do besides setting casualty lists.

2

When I came back I was rather restless. After all the excitement I had in uniform, you seemed drab. I couldn't stand being with you 10 or 12 hours a day, as you demanded.

So I ran off with a cute little portable typewriter and had quite a ball with her in a secluded cabin in the north woods of Wisconsin. Then the money ran out. And, sheepishly, I came back to you.

Then there was that affair with the slick attache case. She

was not a stick-in-the-mud like you. She took me to the best places, swanky offices, with thick carpets and plush drapes. But she was a fussy gal, insisting that I wear a white shirt every day, and a necktie even. I got tired of polishing those tight shoes and attending Dale Carnegie courses.

And so I came back to you, my one and true love, in my baggy slacks, sport shirt, and bedroom slippers.

You greeted me like a jealous wife, splattering hot metal over me. I got so mad I picked up a hammer and knocked a tooth out of your damn mold disk.

Then we simmered down, knowing we were stuck with each other. Sometimes we'd think about the amazing things we had described on the keyboard: crystal radio sets, four-wheel brakes, seven-day Atlantic crossings, short skirts, Volstead, long skirts, Repeal, short skirts, television, filter tips, atomic bombs and tranquilizers, Sally Rand and photographs of Mars. We were grateful for having had the privilege of living in such an interesting era.

And gradually we realized that we were growing old together because of the names appearing in the obituaries. Babe Ruth, Lou Gehrig, Flo Ziegfeld, Douglas Fairbanks, Colonel McCormick, John Barrymore and Ethel and Lionel, Clark Gable and Carole Lombard, Ernest Hemingway and Ben Hecht, Jerome Kern and George Gershwin. Come to think of it, we even set the obituary for Enrico Caruso.

And we're still at it, you and I, pounding the obituaries every day—Kennedy, MacArthur, Churchill, Stevenson, Nat King Cole, Spike Jones, Marilyn Monroe. We're afraid to look at the obituaries for tomorrow.

So maybe it's true that we're too old for tape, both of us. We're just the two of us talking together now, because there's nobody to listen about the days when we were setting the first reviews for the "Student Prince" and the "Vagabond King."

4

Remember the newcomers of that day? Al Jolson, Fred Allen, Houdini. And, of course, there were the movie reviews with Rudy Valentino and Pola Negri. Ages ago, isn't it?

Well, let's face it, old timer. It's about time we got melted down into something else, like old Linotype slugs that get bright new faces every now and then. Maybe you'll come out of the pot as a space capsule and I'll be an astronaut. It doesn't sound right, does it? We're not suited for that kind of razzmatazz.

I'm really the type of guy that should be raking leaves, slowly. And I hope you keep me company in the future, as you did in the past. I don't want to insult you, but I'd like to see you become a shovel or a rake or something like that. A wheelbarrow would be just fine.

Then we could walk together between the hedges of zinnias until we came to the old maple tree. And we'd stretch out in the clover and sleep.

Free Pressmen
Talk Like Free Men

THE wave of refinement which is sweeping the country leaves me gasping for air, like the gopher who finds the wide Missouri pouring down his front door.

Consider the modern pressman, for instance. He looks like a teacher and talks like a minister. Because his labor consists of pushing buttons, he seldom has reason to exercise any profanity.

He would look silly, swearing at a little green button.

One distinguished pressman, the president of a national organization, goes a step farther. He is not satisfied that pressmen have stopped using nasty words. He wants the entire world to stop using them. He wants his colleagues to stop the

7

presses whenever they see a naughty word breaking out in print.

And he is violently opposed to sex. By pressing a button he intends to stop the confusion that Adam started by biting an apple.

Personally, I'm against people who want to stop presses. If you stop them for one thing, you'll have to stop them for other things. Every dictator begins his career by condemning "decadent" literature and winds up by condemning you and me into concentration camps.

If a pressman can act as a censor of sex, then I as a Linotype operator can refuse to set anything pertaining to war. I believe that a military campaign produces more misery than a sexual orgy, and that a Napoleon is more dangerous than a Casanova. I also don't like an avocado, but I give it the freedom to be on a menu.

What surprises me is that the reform movement comes from the ranks of pressmen. It just goes to show you how much they have changed.

The first pressman I knew was Big John. He was the boss of a 12-page Duplex, the kind that prints directly from heavy forms, four full pages to a deck. When Big John loaded the press with more than a thousand pounds of type, he took his position at the big upright lever and stood proud as a captain of a ship. He was the man who got the paper out every day and he knew it. Reporters could get drunk. Linotypers could go berserk, but Big John got the paper out.

One morning I sheepishly asked him, "Mr. Pressman, will you please stop the press?"

"What the hell for?" he demanded. He looked like a giant.

"You've got to take out pages 8 and 9."

"Go away, boy." He told me to do something very shocking.

"I . . . I . . . made up the pages," I said, "and I got something

8

mixed up. I've got to fix them."

He had been getting redder and redder in the cheeks until he exploded like a volcano. I was a block away and still running, but his profanity kept up with me, scorching my tender ears. I realized that with my Sunday school vocabulary I would never make a good printer.

So I tried my luck with a third-rate opera company that was visiting San Francisco. They gave me a job holding a spear on the stage. They smeared my face with tan grease paint and made me wear some kind of Egyptian underwear. At the proper moment I shouted, "Ho, Ho! Ho, Ho!" It was a good performance of "Aida," but the critics made no mention of me. Maybe I should have hollered louder.

I was paid five dollars, which was pretty good money at one dollar per Ho, but I couldn't live on five Ho's a year, so I went back to face the monsters of the print shop.

I made up my mind to learn the language of the pressmen.

I was like poor Eliza Doolittle of "My Fair Lady," learning a new kind of English. The role of Professor Higgins was taken by the pressmen. Day after day they pounded the words into my ears. I became accustomed to the sound.

Gradually I realized that the pressmen were not monsters at all. They were sensitive souls whose blustering speech was a social protest against the hard labor to which they had been condemned.

Since then my sympathies have been with them. I threw away my books and spent my spare time on a bench in the pressroom, listening to them talk. In their virile language they told me more about life than I could ever learn in a library. They used some words that cannot be found in even the most modern literature.

Therefore I doubt that books are responsible for all the evils of the age. I don't think the ancient pressmen learned all the naughty words from books. And they seemed to know quite a lot

9

about the birds and bees, even without a library card. One pressman did admit that he had read two pages of "Evangeline," but I do not recall that she ever used any bad language.

Back in those days nobody was so stupid as to spend 95 cents just to see dirty words in a book. The words used to be carved on wooden fences and outhouse walls, where we could see them for free.

Nowadays we have no wooden fences where the village idiot can exercise his literary talent. So we send him to college where he walks around with a picket sign, showing everybody the kind of word he learned in English Composition II. The really ambitious scribbler once needed a side of a barn for erotic self-expression. Now he writes a thick novel.

Lately I've been buying books again, not because they throw in some dirty words an an inducement, but because the bench in the pressroom is not what it used to be. The language I learned in the pressroom is foreign to modern pressmen. Among those gentle gentlemen I feel like a dinosaur that was resurrected by mistake. So I stay home and read books.

A man's world keeps shrinking and shrinking. There is no place he can go any more.

Burlesque is gone. At the last performance they had women in the audience and pretty boys in the chorus line. The only thing that remained the same was the taffy candy. It was the same candy they couldn't sell for 20 years. They were still trying to sell it.

And the pool hall? Have you been to a pool hall lately? How do you tell the boys from the girls? The hair is the same and the pants are the same. Sometimes the shape of the sweatshirt gives you a clue.

And everybody giggles, boys and girls and the rest of them. How can you figure the angle of a three-cushion shot while some sexually confused eight-ball is giggling over your shoulder?

Maybe this is all a part of that federal employment plan which prohibits discrimination between men and women. Congress has passed a law which says there is no longer any difference between Adam and Eve.

Nevertheless, when I run an advertisement for a model, whom I need while creating magnificent soap sculpture, I do not intend to settle for anything less than a bona fide female. I want a Venus, not a Vincent.

And the pressroom could be full of hazards nowadays despite all the safety devices with fancy buttons and flashing lights. If I sat on that bench and uttered a word in the language of ancient pressmen, I might get slapped in the face.

11

And somebody might scream, "Sir, I want you to know that you're talking to a lady!"

Well, goodbye to the pressroom.

Better I should go back to the opera. And sing in some foreign language where an occasional cuss word will pass unnoticed.

Anybody looking for a grizzly old Mefisto? Have pitchfork. Will travel.

Old-Timers and Tape

THE trouble with us old-timers is that we talk too much about the past. All right, then. Let's talk about the future. The atom bomb . . .

No. Let's talk about the past.

Thirty-eight years ago a vigorous-looking man, slightly graying, walked into our composing room and opened his suitcase on the desk of Mr. Superintendent. He pulled out a yellow roll of punched tape.

"I'm Walter Morey," he introduced himself. "I've been running a Monotype with tape for many years. Now I've invented an attachment which will eliminate the linotype operator."

Mr. Superintendent looked at me, sitting behind the keyboard, straining my good ear towards the conversation.

"There's one operator I'd like to get rid of," he said, jerking a thumb in my direction. "But you forgot one important thing, Mr. Morey. Take a look at our paper. It's not English. It's Bohemian. We've got 15 lower case accents scattered around the keyboard and 15 caps in the pie tray, not to mention the asterisks and cap X's, which also run pie."

I got up from the machine and joined the men at the bench, Profoundly I pointed out, "We also have a couple of umlauts when we set the Slovak dialect, and an o with a roof over it."

Morey, the inventor of the teletypesetter, disconsolately put the tape back into the suitcase.

"I might as well try the Chinese newspapers," he said. He didn't waste any more time on us. He had a great many print shops to visit, trying to sell his idea of a teletypesetter.

There were all kinds of inventors walking the streets those days, selling space band cleaners, matrix cleaners, assembly slide returns, dial thermometers, line counters and miscellaneous gadgets.

Our own Mr. Superintendent was working on a quadder. The jaws were activated by lead weights attached to piano wire. He made a mistake by trying to keep the price under three hundred dollars. He didn't realize that people would be willing to pay two thousand dollars for a good one.

All of these minor inventions were intended merely to increase the efficiency of the operator.

The teletypesetter, however, was in the category of the atom bomb. Its object was to eliminate the operator.

I was one of the panicky ones. I had been quite settled, with ten years of experience at the trade, when I saw the tape for the first time. It worried me. I realized I had to find some other way of making an easy living.

I went back to night school to take lessons on how to be mayor of Chicago, like Tony Cermak did, so I'd have a job to fall back on when I got eliminated by the darn tape.

14

On summer week-ends, I pushed a little hotdog wagon outside of White Sox Park, building up a business so I'd have something to fall back on when I got replaced by the darn tape.

I put a down payment on a small pecan stand on U.S. 1 near St. Augustine, hoping it would keep me alive during the winter months.

Down in Havana I went into partnership with Senora Hermina, who owned a Palace of Pleasure near the yacht harbor. We wanted to open another establishment at Varadero Beach which was becoming popular with American tourists. We planned to buy, eventually, a tropical island a few miles off shore and call it the Garden of Eden. We would charge plenty for letting people make fools of themselves.

It would be something to fall back on when I got replaced by the darn tape.

But Fidel Castro changed our plans. Senora Hermina stayed in Havana, quite confident that she would get a position in Castro's cabinet, probably as Minister of Culture. I went back to Miami, where a letter from Chicago was waiting for me at the post office.

"Dear Otto," it said, "I regret to inform you that you have not yet been replaced by tape. Come back to work, you bum. Your Ex-Boss."

I didn't answer right away. I had planned to take a stroll along the coast of Spain from Malaga through Cartagena and Valencia to Barcelona. From there I'd walk to Marseilles and along the Riviera to Genoa. Of course, I'd visit Florence and Rome and Naples, but I really wanted to spend a lot of time in Albania, where the tough mountaineers eat onions like apples.

However, I went back to Chicago... and from one city to another... one machine to another... waiting... patiently waiting to be replaced by that darn tape. To keep out of mischief, I learned to run an electric typewriter, just in case...

Come to think of it, there is only one way to get along with these modern inventions. A person has to make his own adjustment.

Five centuries ago Gutenberg created a similar problem. His method of printing books with movable type took the jobs away from thousands of scribes who had earned their livelihood by handwriting one book at a time, letter by letter. It was a miserable form of labor that they were doing, but they resented the change. They hated Gutenberg.

The more adaptable ones, however, threw away their goose quills and learned to set type. There was a great demand for typesetters all over Europe because everybody was eager to buy books, now that they were cheap.

When Mergenthaler's first machines made their appearance, 70 years ago, they were not greeted with affection by typesetters. Although the craftsmen worked sixty hours a week for a miserable living, with tuberculosis as a bonus, they resented the machine that threatened their livelihood. The machines were ridiculed and the operators were ostracized because each of these "piano players" was throwing five of his fellow men out of work. But again, some of the more adventurous men quit grumbling and sat down to learn to punch the keys. And they liked it.

The strange part of all this ancient history is that today, after 35 years of the Teletypesetter, there is still a great demand for a Linotyper. And there is also a demand for the typesetter who is an expert at setting by hand. And strangest of all is the fact that even the medieval scribe would find a good job in this modern age. With his skill at calligraphy and ornamental lettering, he could walk into almost any advertising agency and name his price.

Why, Small Printer?

A recent issue of some lithographers' magazine gives the small printer quite a beating. It says he shuffles around the shop with his low IQ dragging. It says he is so dumb that he refuses to follow the brilliant advice given him by a kid fresh out of college.

Young Joe College draws up blue prints and tells the old man how to increase his profits by spending a mere million dollars on new equipment. But the old man, having a low IQ, spends ten dollars on a fishpole and goes in search of bass.

Perhaps the old man is showing a kind of wisdom that they haven't even learned to measure in colleges. IQ tests are for

18

children. Fishpoles are for wise old philosophers.

I've been working for small printers for almost half a century and I've always been impressed by their intelligence. Maybe they don't read Dante, but who the hell does?

To gather more information on the subject, I phoned one of my ex-bosses, a gay bachelor in Chicago, and asked for an interview.

"I want to know why printers go into business," I told him.

"Because they're nuts," he replied. Then he paused, as if taking time to tweak his little white mustache.

"Meet me at the club Sunday," he continued. "It's down in Indiana. We'll have time to talk."

I felt flattered at being invited to his country club. After 50 miles on the hot highway I turned off into a gravel road and stopped at a wooden gate. I was glad I had brought my swimming trunks because I heard people splashing around in a pool.

I fixed my tie, brushed the dandruff off my sport jacket, and followed an attendant to the reception room. I was shocked that the country club was a nudist camp.

For a long time I stood at the window, gathering courage to venture out among the members who were wearing nothing but smiles.

Then I noticed that a man with a tweaked white mustache kept surface-diving into eight feet of water. He'd always come up, flash his body like an albino sea lion as he took a deep breath, and then, with grim determination, he'd dive down again.

I rushed to the pool and dove in after him.

"Hello, Mr. Ex-Boss," I said. "I came for the interview."

"Oh, it's you!" he said, looking real close into my face. "Sorry I didn't recognize you, I'm a mess."

"What's wrong?" I asked, treading water.

"I lost my contact lenses. Both of them. Right here in the pool. And I can't see a thing without them. I'm blind as a bat."

"Blind as a bat in a nudist camp? That's bad, Mr. Boss. I'll try to find the lenses for you."

"It's impossible," he said. "I've been diving for a half hour."

"You stir up too much water. Why don't you go to shore and let me find the lenses?"

The poor man was blue from the cold already and was quite willing to let me take over. Everyone had gone to play volley ball and I had the pool to myself. I waited for the water to settle and then sank to the bottom, perfectly relaxed. I had been practicing Yoga breathing, like Houdini, and could stay on the bottom four or five minutes. Barely moving in the water, I soon found one of the tiny plastic lenses and, a minute later, I saw the other lens floating towards my open fingers. I closed my fist upon it.

Just then, through the greenish water from the bottom of the pool, I saw a body plunging down at me. It was the lady lifeguard, wearing nothing.

I managed to gasp for air as she pulled me out of the pool, but got a mouthful of water and began choking. She insisted on giving me artificial respiration and then flipped me over and tried mouth to mouth resuscitation, peppermint flavor.

A gruff voice in the crowd said, "That old guy ain't dead. He's blushing. Dead men don't blush."

Innocently I looked into her big blue eyes.

"Fink!" she said. And she walked away, indignantly waggling her sun-tanned hips.

"Here's your contact lenses, Mr. Boss," I said.

"Thanks," he replied, adjusting them to the scenery. "You can have your job back if you teach me Yoga breathing."

"All I want is an interview. I want to know how you got yourself involved in a printing business. Was it a life-long ambition? Did you analyze the market, the way they do in colleges? What did you really do that actually put you into business?"

He stretched out in the chaise lounge and let the sun beat down on his smiling face, crowned with luxuriant white hair.

"The most important thing I did," he said meditatively, "was to punch a production manager in the nose. He kept pushing me around and I didn't like it. So I punched him in the nose, real hard. I just didn't like being pushed around. So I went into business for myself. That's why most printers have gone into business. They just got tired of being pushed around."

I shook my head. "But that's not an intelligent reason for going into business. That's emotional."

"Emotions are important," he said. "Take love, for instance. All the engineers in the world can't analyze love, but it's real nevertheless. People get killed over it. And there's no way to analyze the feeling of a man who doesn't like to be pushed around."

"You've got a point, Mr. Boss. But look at it this way. If you hadn't gone into business you might have been an executive of a big corporation, making more money, and having your own private washroom key."

"But I wouldn't be happy. I'd have to worry about the kind of clothes I wore on Sunday, to keep up the good image of the corporation. Being my own boss, I don't have to wear a thing. And this is the way I like it."

Our attention was attracted to the diving board where a statuesque blonde was standing on tip-toe. She was wearing a sexy, black lace peek-a-boo swimming suit. She executed a graceful swan-dive and as she swam to the edge of the pool, the energetic lady life-guard started to bawl her out.

"This is a respectable nudist camp!" she was shouting. "I'll have you thrown out of here this minute if you don't get out of that nasty, lascivious swimming suit."

21

The blonde climbed out of the water, folded her arms on her voluminous chest, and stared right back at the nude lady life-guard.

"Lay a hand on me," she said, "and I'll slam you in the kisser. And if you don't like it, I'll start my own camp on the other side of the river. And I'll let the customers wear anything they damn please. I'll put this crummy joint out of business."

Mr. Ex-Boss sat up, joyfully twitching his mustache. He was happy to listen to the shouting of angry women. They made him glad he had remained a bachelor.

"That life-guard would make a good production manager," he said. "She's fresh out of college and wants everything to go according to the rule book. She's really on the ball. She even checked the time on her wristwatch before diving into the water after you. But that gal in the black lace is something different. She's egocentric. She's the kind that will go into business for herself. She'll make her own rules."

"Amen," I said, watching the battling girls tugging at each other. "Right now she's losing her shirt."

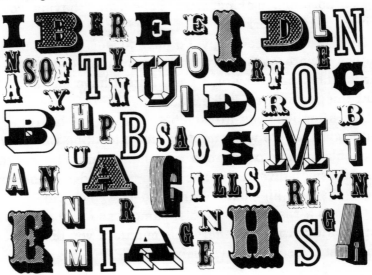

If I Had a Million

"IF I had a million dollars . . . If I had a million dollars . . . I wouldn't have to be a slave to a newspaper . . ."

I was only a kid that time, dreaming of wealth the way kids do, while bending over a make-up table. I was filling out the pages of a Bohemian daily newspaper with leads and slugs after the make-up man had put the type and cuts into place.

The job was alright, for twelve dollars a week, but surely there was more to life than just putting out a newspaper every day. If I had a million...

I looked across the table into the sad eyes of an old man who had stopped to watch me work. Shrunken with age, he was just tall enough to plant his elbows on the make-up table and rest his

23

chin on interlocked knuckles. Under his lower lip was a tiny gray goatee.

It was August Geringer, the publisher, 85 years old. According to rumors, he was worth a million.

"In the old days," he was saying, "it took longer to space a form. Hand type was hard to handle."

I merely nodded. How does a kid talk to a millionaire? To a man who was born 20 years before the Civil War? I was proud he had even noticed me.

Every morning at ten o'clock, wearing his traditional carpet slippers, this old gentleman would shuffle into the composing room to make sure his newspaper got out on time.

When the twelve pages were finally locked in the Duplex and the press began to roll, Mr. Geringer reached into his lower left vest pocket for a thin wooden snuff box. He put a pinch of the powdered tobacco on the back of his veined hand and took an epicurean sniff with each nostril.

The snuff, he insisted, kept him free of all disease. He never went to see doctors. If they sometimes came to see him, at his family's insistence, he would listen to their advice and then continue to do as he pleased.

When one doctor prescribed eye glasses, Mr. Geringer complied by wearing the glasses at all times— in the vest pocket above the snuff. Another doctor recommended dentures, which promptly were assigned to the right side of the vest, the uppers in the upper pocket, the lowers in the lower.

Mr. Geringer had raised and educated a fine family of four and could have had a comfortable life with any of his children, enjoying the luxuries of suburban living, but he preferred to remain in the small apartment above the newspaper plant, close to his work.

He was at his desk before six every morning, reading the hand-written copy from his correspondents, many of whom had been loyal to him for half a century. Through the years, from

1875 when his Daily Svornost was founded, these letters had been a living history of immigration in America. They had come from the mud huts of Nebraska prairies, from the homesteaders of Kansas and the Dakotas, and from the less fortunate people who were hopelessly trapped in the sweat shops of an alien culture.

Mr. Geringer also took care of the payroll of the entire publishing firm, putting the proper amount of cash into the envelope of each of his 40 employees. At that time there were no deductions of any kind. There was a sacredness in a man's salary that put it beyond the reach of politicians.

Just before noon the old gentleman would slowly walk up the stairs to his apartment for dinner and a nap. Sometimes he would bring a book for his housekeeper to let her decide whether or not it should be published in serial form in one of his publications. He knew that if she kept reading it while the potatoes were burning, the other housewives would also like it.

25

Late in the afternoon he came downstairs again to look over the afternoon mail. Then he would take a final walk through the composing room to see that everything was in order. He never failed to stoop down to pick a Linotype matrix off the floor.

"This little piece of brass," he explained, "is worth seven cents."

He could not tolerate waste of any kind, especially the waste of time. He kept prodding us boys to keep going to night school. He had been a teacher in the old country and always regarded himself more of a teacher than a business man.

But he did not live entirely without luxuries. Although he did not care for fancy cars or yachts, he did enjoy sitting back in his rocking chair, unhurriedly enjoying the delicacy of rye bread with liederkrantz cheese.

Inasmuch as I was also the errand boy, it became my duty to buy the cheese for him. It was not just any old liederkrantz cheese. It was a special cheese made in Milwaukee and sold only in one small delicatessen in Chicago's loop.

The first time I was sent to buy it, one of the older boys took me aside and said, "Lissen, dummy. That stinkin' cheese is the same no matter where it's made. We always buy the stuff right here, in the delicatessen down the block. No use draggin' it 10 miles on a hot street car. He'll never know the difference."

I shook my head. "The boss told me to buy it downtown. On LaSalle Street."

While I was running all the other errands downtown, I tried to convince myself that I should do as the other boys did. But my "old country" discipline took me to the LaSalle Street shop.

Cellophane wrapping had not yet been invented and the two-pound lump of aromatic cheese quite forcefully spread its questionable charm through the ordinary wrapping paper. In the hot crowded trolley I stood alone, ostracized by humanity.

wondering why the trolley couldn't go faster.

When I delivered the package to Mr. Geringer, he thanked me quite simply. I realized I had been a fool for going through the trolley car ordeal. I could have bought the smelly stuff in the delicatessen down the block.

But next day, as he rested his elbows on the make-up table, there was a twinkle in his eyes as he looked at me.

"That was good cheese you brought yesterday," he said. "It's the real liederkrantz. Made in Milwaukee."

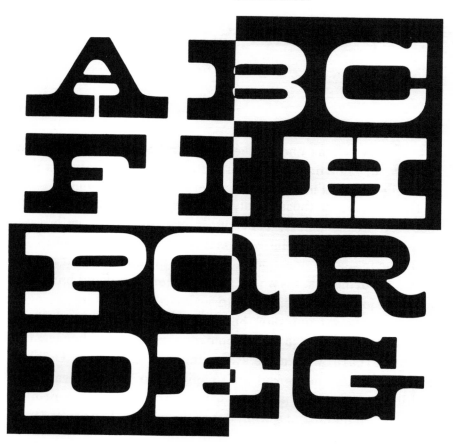

Speak and Squeak Softly

MARVIN was one of the most kind-hearted men I've ever known. When he caught a butterfly he always let it go, believing that life in any form was extremely precious.

He was one of those lonely printers who wander about the country, living simply, becoming more and more withdrawn from society because he was having trouble with his ears. He could hear some voices, but not others; high sounds but not low ones. Nevertheless, he was a good printer who could have held a steady job anywhere, if he had so desired.

One day he sat on a park bench in Omaha, wondering whether to hitch-hike east to make some money, or go farther west, to Santa Barbara, where the swimming is wonderful in October. Still undecided, he picked up a copy of the World-Herald, discarded by someone, and saw a want-ad asking for a printer. Obeying an impulse, he went down the hill to Thirteenth Street and stopped at the door of the print shop.

He was astonished to see such lovely pink drapes in the win-

dow. As he opened the door, his poor ears were treated to the sound of Oriental chimes which plinked do-mi-sol-do, do-sol, do-sol. He would have turned back, feeling he had stumbled into the wrong place, had it not been for the clanking of a Gordon press. A woman was running it.

Shutting off the machine, she turned to face Marvin. Despite her masculine attire—slacks, shirt and a cap—Marvin could see that she was quite a woman, all the way down. A few blonde curls crept from under her cap across her ink-stained forehead.

"You're a printer?" she asked, hopefully.

Marvin nodded. He was a good-lip reader and those were beautiful lips to read.

"I'm hard of hearing," he said. "You'll have to speak a bit louder."

"Oh," she seemed disappointed. Then she continued. "My husband died, almost a year ago. And I've been trying to keep the business going. It's tough."

Marvin studied the Miehle Vertical, standing clean and idle. He winced as he saw all those undistributed forms on the slanted tops of the type cabinets and he didn't like those flower pots around the presses. He felt a sudden urge to go to California, but he felt sorry for this poor widow, stuck with a print shop. A horrible fate for any woman.

"I'm an all-around printer," he said finally. "I'll help you out."

"I'm so glad," she said, taking off her cap and letting her blonde hair fall loose to her shoulders. "I'm pretty good at setting type," she said modestly, "but when it comes to presses, I get scared."

"I can run any press," said Marvin. "Real good. Want me to start now?"

She looked at the clock, "It's almost four already. We'll let it

30

go for tomorrow. Have a cup of coffee?"

From the apartment in back of the shop she brought an electric coffee pot and a tray of cookies. They stood at the make-up table, eating and talking, for more than an hour. Now and then Marvin gave a cookie to a white poodle who had taken a liking to him.

The Lady Boss nodded in satisfaction. "A dog is a good judge of character," she said.

Marvin was on the job fifteen minutes early the next morning. The Lady Boss wore a simple yellow dress, but she filled it like an Italian movie star. She needed no nylons to enhance the beauty of her smoothly shaven legs.

"You're early," she said to Marvin. "I'm just having breakfast. Care to join me?"

"I ate," said Marvin.

"Another cup of coffee won't hurt you."

He followed her to the kitchen. It was a neat, cozy little apartment she had back there, a harbor of femininity where the morning sun filtered through ruffled white curtains and where the fragrance of apple pie made a man wish he had a home of his own.

In one brief moment of introspection, Marvin regretted all the years he had spent in aimless wandering. In the woman's large brown eyes he saw the dawn of a new life.

"Show me what you want done," he said, rising from the table. "I can work better than any two men."

She led the way into the shop with a spring in her step, as if she, too, saw the hope of a better future.

"Start with these dance tickets," she said. "Print a thousand of them. And then these statements . . ."

While he studied the job tickets, she added, "I'll be back in a couple of hours. I have to see a few customers. I've been neglecting them."

While locking the form in the Gordon and spreading the ink on the rollers, Marvin's mind was on the Lady Boss all the time. Strong with new found power, he would show her what a great printer he really could be.

He had run off almost a hundred tickets when he heard a squeak. He threw in the safety lever and listened. Squeak. Sounded like a bearing. Women never remember that a machine needs oil. He shut off the press and looked for an oil can, which he finally found behind a pot of geraniums. He gave the old Gordon a real good oil job.

Confidently he threw the switch, increasing the speed to make up for lost time.

Squeak.

He slowed down. Squeak, Squeak.

He shut off the press again, looked around for a wire, and began digging the dirt out of the oil holes. That poor Lady Boss never thought of cleaning such important things; she was too busy cleaning windows.

An hour was gone and he still had only 150 cards printed, but with a bit of speed he'd get them all out before she came back.

Squeak. Squeak. Squeak. That would be just his luck, to burn out a bearing the first day on the job.

He stopped again, mad at himself for becoming so filthy from crawling around that darn press. He knew he had ink on his cheeks and oil in his hair, but he had no time to wash. He oiled everything once more and desperately started the press again.

Squeak.

On his hands and knees he stared into the mechanism of the slowly idling press. Only two hundred dance tickets in two hours. For the best boss in the world.

Squeak.

He saw it. Through a gap in the slowly moving cams he saw it. It was in a cage against the wall, next to the rubber plant.

32

Marvin really did love all living creatures, but as he was kneeling on the floor, frustrated, dirty, oily, ink-stained and way behind schedule, his hand instinctively reached for a mallet. And when that canary went squeak, squeak, in obvious derision, Marvin let the mallet fly.

He didn't hurt the bird. He only put a dent in the cage. But quite a few yellow feathers were flying around when the Lady Boss came running across the shop.

"Poor Birdie Boy!" she was shrieking. "Are you hurt? By that horrible brute?"

Marvin washed up slowly, taking a farewell sniff of apple pie.

And he walked out into the street, sadly reflecting that even the noblest aspirations of man can be loused up by a little canary.

33

You Can Better Yourself

OCCASIONALLY every Linotype operator suffers a fit of insanity. He develops a yearning to wear a white shirt and a necktie. And he wants to carry a briefcase. He says good-bye to the grumpy old Linotype and goes out to conquer the white collar world.

Old Man Moses was such a Linotyper. After 40 years at the machine he decided to try a new career. He bought a briefcase and became a teacher.

"But why?" I asked him.

"My secret ambition," he replied. "Ever since I dropped out of grammar school I've wanted to be a teacher. I've been studying in my spare time."

"But you're taking a big cut in salary," I protested.

34

"Money isn't everything," said Old Man Moses, with a dreamy look in his eyes.

His mind was made up. He got a haircut and bought six white shirts. Then he added up his credits from the numerous colleges he had attended during his wanderings. There was medieval history from CCNY, modern poetry from Northwestern, Balkan anthropology from Berkeley and scientific hog breeding from the University of Iowa. By mixing all these ingredients he came out with a certificate which entitled him to teach offset printing.

"I'm as surprised as anybody," he confided to me. "I've never run an offset press in my life. But I'll learn fast, After all, it can't be more difficult than Sanskrit."

In bouncing around newspapers all over the country, Old Man Moses had seen presses half a block long. Now he was in charge of a press no bigger than a peanut stand. But he grew proud of it.

"This little press," he told his students, "can save the country from tyranny. It is with presses like this that democracy can be preserved. The big presses, like radio and television, will be the first to fall under a dictator's control. But these little presses, hidden in barns and basements, will keep carrying the torch of freedom."

Old Man Moses paused to let his eloquence sink in.

"Our basement got a leak," said one of the boys. "When it rains we need a rowboat."

A Negro boy raised his hand.

"A question?" asked Moses hopefully.

"I gotta go to the washroom," the boy replied.

Mr. Moses nodded permissively.

"As I was saying," he continued, "the small press is the guardian of democracy. It won our freedom in the past and it will preserve our freedom for tomorrow."

"Tomorrow I gotta stay home," a boy interrupted. "I gotta

watch the kids. Ma's gonna go downtown to look for a job."

"Bring a note."

"She can't write English."

"Have her write it in Spanish."

Mr. Moses took a long breath as he tried to remember where he had left off. "Without the printing press we would still be living in ignorance, in fear, and in slavery. Some day many of you boys will be out in the world, working in print shops. I want you to remember one thing. You will be doing more than merely earning a living. You will be doing something far more import- ant. You will be building a civilization."

Old Man Moses studied the faces of the boys, hoping to find a spark of interest. But all the boys were looking at the clock. The bell shattered the silence and in ten seconds Old Man Moses stood alone.

He shrugged tolerantly. He used to be a clock-watcher him- self. Tomorrow he'd start the lecture earlier so that he'd get in the good points before the boys got restless. He would tell them how the Roman Empire was held together by papyrus, even as our own government is held together by millions of reams of paper.

A telephone rang in the closet.

"Mr. Moses?"

"Yes?"

"That man who visited the shop yesterday was an inspector. He filed a complaint in the district office."

"Complaint? About what?"

"Ink smudges on the side of your press. Black fingerprints."

Mr. Moses paused as he tried to remember. Then he said, "The boys were cleaning the rollers when the inspector came in. They had ink on their hands."

"That's a very expensive piece of machinery, Mr. Moses. More than three thousand dollars."

"I realize that, sir. But a fingerprint won't hurt it. We clean the press at the end of the period. We take ten minutes for clean-up."

"Take a half hour, Mr. Moses. Get every fingerprint off the press."

"But we need more time for teaching . . ."

The phone clicked.

Old Man Moses went to look at the press. Yes, there were fingerprints on it. Carefully, he began wiping them off. The trouble with teaching, he told himself, is that you get involved with the kids. It's easy to tell a boss to go to hell and walk out on him, but how do you walk out on your gang of kids? How do you

walk out on Jimmie who has come to regard you as a father, the only father he ever had?

But you can't keep wiping fingerprints off presses all your life. You're a man and have to do a man's work. You can't be a wet nurse forever.

Old Man Moses tossed the smudged rag into a can and washed his hands. He glared across the room at the contemptible black briefcase, the symbol of an old man's vanity. It was full of lectures about printing which he had intended to deliver. Now he realized that nobody gave a damn about anything. The kids came to his class just to waste time, or to do the boogaloo to the rhythm of the press.

He picked up the briefcase and decided to tell the principal that he was through. They could easily get a substitute.

He was at the door when little Pedro came barging in.

"Mr. Moses," he shouted shrilly as he dug into a stack of printed paper. "Mr. Moses, I'm looking for some of that stuff I printed this morning."

"What do you want with it?"

"I wanna show my mother the kind of work I can do. That's real good printing, ain't it, Mr. Moses?"

A smile crept across the teacher's face.

"Sure is, Pedro. Tomorrow we'll try some color work. Red and black on the same paper."

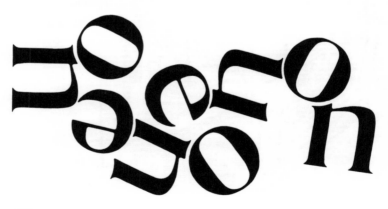

Days of Dreams and Hunger

BACK in the days of my foolish youth I bought an old Intertype and decided to become a captain of the typesetting industry. Within a few weeks I had to choose between feeding myself and feeding metal into the Intertype. Both of us were hungry. And so I bought another hundred pounds of metal.

Business was hard to get in those days, especially when I had nothing to offer except four fonts of Cheltenham with hairlines. I was able to work cheap because my overhead was low. My heating plant consisted of a small iron stove that used to fall apart now and then, spilling hot coals on the floor. I always kept a bucket of water beside it. In extremely cold weather I kept my feet wrapped in blankets while I pounded away at the keyboard.

Bills were piling up, customers weren't paying and I was ready to quit when an old gentleman walked into the shop. He was elegantly dressed, from gray spats to a genuine silk top hat. Graciously he took off the stove-pipe hat, carefully put his white scarf into it, and slowly peeled suede gloves off his blue-veined hands.

"I've heard that you're a typesetter," he said in the clipped Oxford English of Ronald Coleman. "I am Mr. Queekie, an author. I publish my own books."

"I'd be glad to do your typesetting," I said. "I specialize in books. I run night and day, just setting books."

I showed him samples of my four type faces. He agreed that ten-point would be all right, on an 11-point slug.

He opened a package and showed me a manuscript for a novel. I gulped when I considered the financial problems of setting the book.

As if he understood, he extracted two crisp $20 bills from his wallet. He said he would be back in a few days to look at the proofs and pay me more money.

"I've inherited a tea plantation in India," he explained casually.

He came to the shop every Tuesday and Friday, always with two crisp $20 bills. In those days, money went a long way.

Sometimes I felt guilty about taking the money. I was convinced that the novel was corny, but I didn't have the courage to tell him.

"What do you think of the book?" he'd always ask.

"Pretty good," I'd be forced to reply. "It's quite different from other books."

"I'm going to sell it to Hollywood," he said. "I'm already contacting beautiful girls to play the role of Myrtle."

"Myrtle gets killed," I pointed out, anxious to impress him with my deep study of his book.

40

He nodded. "It will be the only time in Hollywood history that a girl will get her head chopped off right in front of the camera. It will not be a dummy or a double. It will be a real Myrtle, as real as the axe."

I shook my head. "Where will you get a girl to play the part?" I asked.

"Any healthy American girl will be glad to lose her head for the privilege of being a movie star. I've got fifteen candidates already, eager to be glamorized in cinematic history. It's better than letting their lives go down the kitchen sink."

Before the book got off the presses, Mr. Queekie brought another bundle of typewritten copy. I looked through the pages, shaking my head.

"It's a dictionary," he explained, "in which the words are listed backwards. For instance, the first word is baa, because it ends with two a's. It will be listed as aab. One of the last words is Auschwitz because it ends with z. It will be listed as ztiwhcsuA."

"But what's the advantage of such a dictionary?" I asked timidly.

"It's original," he answered, staring me straight in the eyes. "Nobody ever tried it before."

It wasn't an easy job setting a dictionary in which the words were inverted, but the crisp $20 bills were keeping me alive. Then I got a bellyache which turned out to be acute appendicitis.

I lay in the hospital ward with 13 other patients. Reconciled to bankruptcy, I finally found time to read "War and Peace."

But, at every opportunity, my eyes wandered from the verbiage of Tolstoy to the undulating hip movement of Gwendolyn, the beautiful blonde nurse. This morning she was coming toward me, carrying a huge bouquet of red roses. To my surprise, she stopped at my bed.

She showed me the card. "To my publisher," it said. "Get well soon. From Mr. Queekie, Author."

Gwendolyn had taken my pulse a few times before, but had never shown any interest in its quickened tempo. This time, after settling the roses in a vase, she held my wrist for a thousand beats.

"I didn't know you were a publisher," she whispered in a throaty tone.

I would have laughed, but I was afraid of splitting the stitches. So I merely patted her hand.

Suddenly I was getting a lot of attention. The nurses kept washing me as if I were a prize exhibit.

In the afternoon there was a hush throughout the ward as Mr. Queekie appeared at the door, holding his top hat like a duke expecting obeisance. A retinue of fluttering nurses followed him to my bed. Solemnly he unwrapped a package which contained a dozen cloth-bound copies of his novel about Myrtle. With a masterful flourish of penmanship he was autographing the books and passing them to the nurses. Holding up his hand to silence the commotion, he announced that he was looking for a beautiful girl to play the part of Myrtle in Hollywood.

Then he nodded toward me and said that I was financially involved in the film. He explained that I was having my appendix removed incognito because I liked to play poor, to avoid publicity. Then, putting on his gloves, he said that he had to catch the Santa Fe Chief for Hollywood.

A flock of nurses escorted him to the elevator and then came back to stare at me.

Gwendolyn put screens around my bed as if staking a claim. She kept fussing over me, taking my temperature, fixing my pillow, bending over me, tantalizing me with her bountiful feminine attributes. Every few minutes I would reward her with

42

another rose, one at a time.

She wanted to accompany me home as a private nurse, but I didn't want her to see my shabby room, nor my ridiculous type-setting establishment. She wrote her phone number on the inside cover of Tolstoy and sealed it with the lipstick imprint of her luscious lips. I promised to take her to dinner in a week or so, maybe to Palm Beach.

At the shop the unpaid bills were stacked high and I needed ten spacebands. I didn't have the nerve to call Gwendolyn. I decided to wait until I became more prosperous.

So instead of taking her to dinner I bought the ten spacebands.

That just goes to show you that I was quite an idiot when I was young.

That's the Printing Business

IN this jet age it's the far-away place that glitters with glamor. It's a matter of prestige to get suavely clipped in a gambling joint in San Juan or to stick your fingers into that gluey goo-goo at Waikiki. And it's nice to be able to talk about the interesting people you've met in Rio or Bombay, like that kindergarten teacher from Council Bluffs or the sanitation engineer from Hoboken.

But there's a lot to be seen right here at home. Take the state of Indiana, for instance, It's neither glamorous nor spectacular, but there's a comfortable coziness in the very names of cities like Kokomo and Terre Haute, and a muted reminder of Indian lore in rivers like Kankakee and Tippecanoe.

The rolling hills of Indiana have cradled some of the great

men of American journalism, while the lovely banks of the Wabash have inspired some of our most beautiful songs, including Star Dust. The natives of Indiana, as a rule, become attached to their land. They form the backbone of the nation.

Therefore, to get the feeling of the real America, I like to wander down the Hoosier state, from the steel and vice of the north, past the blushing nudism of Roselawn, down to the towns where farmers gather on wooden benches on Saturday night while their wives do the weekly shopping. There are still a few movie houses where kids whoop it up with popcorn and bubble gum during Sunday matinees, glad to get away from the confinement of television in the parental living room.

Last summer, as I was meandering south, I poked my nose into a print shop in central Indiana. It wasn't much of a printing plant, only 20 by 30, made of gray concrete blocks. But its name, Bonanza Printing Co., intrigued an old prospector like me.

The only person in the shop was a young man with a cute mustache. He was sitting at a desk, poking into a typewriter.

"Sorry," I said. "I thought this was a print shop. I happen to be looking for a few days of work."

"You're a printer?" he asked, seeming genuinely interested. "What kind of mn . . . mn. . . mn. . ."

"You'll have to speak louder, sir. I'm hard of hearing, but I can run almost any kind of equipment. . ."

I wanted to explain that my deafness was only temporary, depending on the humidity. Foggy weather always clogged up my sinus, or something. Otherwise I could hear pretty good.

But the fine young man was shaking my hand. "It's all right," he was hollering loud enough to disturb the hogs across the highway. "You may be just the man we're looking for. I believe in hiring handicapped people. They don't goof around."

And he took me to the shop beyond the partition. The equipment consisted of a worm-eaten type cabinet with fonts of Cheltenham, Gallia, and Comstock. The 10x15 press might have been

46

the masterpiece of George Phineas Gordon back in 1872.

The phone rang and Mr. Boss excused himself. He came back with an order he had just jotted down. It called for 250 bingo tickets to be delivered the following week.

Worriedly I gave the press a trial run, hoping it wouldn't collapse. Then I picked up the composing stick and wondered how I was going to support the whole shebang with 250 bingo tickets.

But business was picking up. Mr. Boss kept talking on the phone, taking in all kinds of orders. Now and then I'd hear something about 10,000 circulars, 50,000 ballots, and 5000 copies of a political newspaper. I was getting worried. The guy might be nuts.

He was all smiles, however, rather cute in his mustache, and he didn't complain if it took me a half day to run off 250 bingo tickets. For the rest of the week he kept giving me calling cards and things like that, just enough to pay my salary.

In his station wagon, meanwhile, he was dragging in bundles from all kinds of places. To every bundle he would attach the gold and red label of the Bonanza Printing Co. and send it right out again. Within a month he had to hire a good-looking blonde to help him with the billing, labeling, and bookkeeping.

Now and then she'd go out for a ride with a politician who seemed to be a very good customer.

One day Mr. Boss gave me a quart of brandy.

"We're going to have some inspectors here day after tomorrow," he said in the loud voice he always used on me. "Don't talk to anybody. Just act deaf and dumb."

"O.K., sir," I replied, using the finger language I had learned in the composing room of the Chicago Tribune.

Next day I helped him unload three offset duplicators he had borrowed somewhere. I plugged them in, leveled them off, and got them rolling, using the aluminum plates he had brought along.

47

When the inspectors came there were three temporary employees in the shop, hired just for that day. They didn't know one end of a press from another. All they did was flick the switch and try to stack the paper. I did all the rest. After the inspection Mr. Boss gave each of them ten dollars and told them thanks.

There was a tinkling of glasses in the office as Mr. Boss and Mr. Politician were laughing. Even the blonde was giggling.

"We made quite an impression, didn't we?" said Mr. Boss. "It looked like a real busy shop. I'll have to return those duplicators tomorrow. They're not even bolted down."

I was getting rather disgusted with my job. I knew that Mr. Boss was a broker and that the shop was merely a front. He was bidding on all kinds of political work and farming it out for the lowest prices he could get.

One day there was a hassle in the office.

"You can't bluff them forever!" Mr. Politician said. "You've got to get some real equipment in here. Besides, we could bid on a lot more work. . ."

"Keep your voice down," said Mr. Boss "D'you think I enjoy riding all over Indiana, Illinois, and Kentucky, chiseling the starving printers? Sure I'd like to have the equipment right here. But I'm not going to risk MY money."

"It's government work, ain't it?" said Mr. Politician. "Let the government put up the money."

And so Mr. Boss packed his journals, ledgers, invoices, and the blonde secretary into his station wagon and went to the big city to get a loan. I overheard that he expected at least a half million, considering the tremendous volume of his rapidly growing enterprise.

But I had an old-fashioned feeling that the government was not going to loan a young whippersnapper a half million dollars, even if he did have a cute mustache. And I was right. It took a lot of overnight trips to the metropolis before he finally got his loan, a very disappointing loan, nowhere near a half million. He had to settle for a mere $225,000, which, of course, is peanuts.

The shop really began humming with salesmen, eager to un-load all kinds of equipment on credit. They were selling every-thing—letterpress, offset, hot type, cold type, film type, and beautiful yellow ribbons of tape. I felt rather silly, running my little bingo tickets in a corner. And new employees were being hired to run the equipment, at double my salary. One day my press was sent to a museum.

"You're still one of the team, Otto," Mr. Boss assured me. "We've promoted you to superintendent of maintenance." And he handed me a brand new broom.

"Sorry, sir," I said. "It's getting cold in Indiana. I'm hanker-ing to follow the birds down south."

He didn't seem unhappy about my leaving.

"In that case I'll pay your wages right now," he said. And from the filing cabinet he gave me a full quart of brandy to remember him by.

Image in a Crystal Ball

WE called him the Guru because his gaunt face was covered by a bramble bush beard and he usually remained aloof. He wore a Nehru shirt most of the time, blue or black, with a brass chain necklace which he tucked under the high collar when leaning over the forms of the financial pages.

He was a very good make-up man and worked real fast, as if he had six hands like one of those funny statues in India. When he finished he would stand silent, in deep meditation.

"You're just the type of person," I told him, "who should know something about ESP."

The Guru's hollowed eyes clouded with a mist.

"I live in the other world," he said, "more than in this one. Through the years of meditation I have found my way into the infinity beyond sensory perception. In fact, when I am making up those pages of the Daily Bugle, the headlines seem old to me.

51

I've seen them already... yesterday... last week... last month..."

My eyes were drawn to the brass pendant he was twirling with hypnotic effect.

"D'you mean to tell me," I whispered in amazement, "that you see the stock market reports a month ahead of time? You could make a million."

"Financial matters do not interest me," said the Guru, bending over a form to make some corrections. "Money is a transitory thing, here today, gone tomorrow."

I suspected the Guru was just giving me a line. So the next day I brought a two-dollar crystal ball to the lunchroom and put it on the table where the Guru was feasting, as usual, on nothing but walnuts and dates.

"Tell us, Guru," I said. "What do you see?"

Calmly cracking a walnut, he replied. "Cheap crystal ball. Sears Roebuck bargain basement."

A crowd had gathered around the table. Even a few lady proofreaders were staring into the crystal ball, as if they expected to see a husband lurking inside.

The twittering was silenced by the deep voice of O'Malley, the stereotyper. "Who's gonna win the Kentucky Derby?" he demanded.

The Guru absently kept nibbling a walnut. "I do not concern myself with horses," he said. "Sacred cows, yes, but not horses. Besides, it's not my crystal ball."

And he pointed a long, skinny finger at me.

"All right then, Yogi man." O'Malley addressed me. "What do you see in the crystal ball? Who's gonna win the Derby tomorrow?"

Quite frankly, I don't know too much about four-legged fillies. I didn't even know the names of the entries because I don't do much Linotyping for the sport section. And I was worried that O'Malley might beat me up if I gave him the wrong tip. So I tried

52

to corn my way out of a difficult situation.

With a nostalgic smile on my face, I said. "I see Sally Rand in the crystal ball. She's dancing with two big fans made of ostrich feathers. One in front and one in back. And she's wearing nothing else."

A lady proofreader snorted.

"Dirty old man!" she exclaimed indignantly. And with her pointed chin high in the air she click-clacked out of the lunchroom.

An apprentice kept staring into his racing form.

"I don't see no Sally Rand in this paper," he complained. "She must of got scratched. Or maybe you ain't got that thing tuned in to Kentucky. Maybe you went too far into the future and got Pimlico by mistake. But even then, I never heard of..."

"I really do see Sally Rand," I insisted, feeling sorry for the uncultured oaf who so obviously had been deprived of the elegant refinements of yesteryear. "Ooops, she almost dropped a fan."

Everybody had suddenly developed an interest in the terpsichorean art. They were elbowing each other aside to peek into the revealing crystal ball.

Once again O'Malley's voice silenced the confusion.

"Quiet!" he roared. "The Yogi says he sees Sally Rand. He sees the image of a dancer. The winner of the derby will be..."

The lunchroom cleared in ten seconds flat as everybody ran down to the mailing room to place bets on Dancer's Image. Even one of the big shot editors was there, standing in line, clutching a ten-dollar bill. He hadn't even finished writing his editorial on the evils of gambling.

Well, Dancer's Image won the Derby, as you know. And even though there was some argument over the kind of aspirin she had been taking, people who had bet on her got to keep their money just the same. And the employees of the Daily Bugle kept tossing dollar bills at me, asking me to look into the crystal ball to see what I could see. I became known as Yogi Otto, a peculiar title, if I say so myself.

But the Guru kept shaking his head.

"Phony crystal ball," he maintained. "My ESP tells me you should sell it before you get killed."

I figured he was jealous. Then I took another look at his new chain necklace. It wasn't brass. It was gold. And I took a double blink at the green rock in his pendant. I had been chasing rich widows long enough to recognize a real emerald when I saw one.

I suspected there might be some sweet connection between the Guru's ESP and the financial pages of the Daily Bugle. To show him I respected his advice I sold the crystal ball to O'Malley for twenty dollars. And I made a determined effort to become the lonely Guru's best friend, maybe even his partner.

I did some reading on Brahma, Vishnu, and Shiva, which did me no harm. I memorized a few philosophical passages from the Upanishads and learned to count up to ten in Sanskrit— eka, dvi, tri, catur, panca, sas, sapta, asta, nava, dasa. And I began eating walnuts and dates for a five-minute lunch.

But my greatest achievement was learning to stand on my head in the shower room, next to the Guru, for a few minutes of deep Oriental meditation.

During one of these sessions he confided that he needed a partner in the little business he had as a sideline. He needed someone to watch the store while he entertained the blonde who had suddenly come into his life. She was very beautiful, he said, not the type to mope around in sad neglect. Now and then she'd go to the beach with some bum who had plenty of time on his hands.

"Why don't you quit this job at the newspaper?" I asked.

"You seem to be making plenty of money at the other place."

"No," said the Guru, shaking his foot because he couldn't shake his head while standing on it. "My job here is necessary to my business. But things would go better if I had a Linotypist for a partner. I wouldn't have to be asking the old crabs to set lines for me. And maybe you could take care of my customers at the store while I'd be attending to important business elsewhere."

"I'd be glad to." I said.

"O.K. But you'll have to learn to wear a turban."

The Guru worked the late afternoon shift at the Daily Bugle, which gave him the greater part of the day to devote to his little store on the west side. In the store he would sit on a high velvet cushion beyond a huge crystal ball and mumble Oriental sounds while his long, exotic fingers touched the trembling hand of a lady customer. Almost always he managed to envisage some glamorous prince lurking in the future, eager to carry the woman across the threshold of the Taj Mahal, or at least pay last month's rent in the slum.

There were men customers, too, with problems that were more mathematical than romantic. They were interested in lucky numbers.

"I've got a good steady business," the Guru told me. "But I hate to think of all the money my customers are spending elsewhere. I'd like to expand into the numbers racket myself, but I need a partner, preferably a linotyper at the Bugle who could cast me a line now and then."

"Count me out," I said, knifing a finger across my throat. "There's four gangs handling baseball attendance numbers and three more specializing in the daily federal deficit. They don't like competition."

"Those numbers are too closely watched," said the Guru. "Anybody can find them in any newspaper in the country. But do you know how many sacred cows were sacrificed in the local stock yards yesterday... cattle slaughtered, that is?"

I shook my head.

"Well, the Bugle is the only newspaper that carries that figure. Our dear, departed publisher used to be a cowpoke as well as a stickler for accuracy. So every day we carry, in agate type, the exact number of cows that were clonked, right on the head."

The Guru flicked a ladybug off the crystal ball as he continued. "That magic number is on the financial page, under my jurisdiction. You, as a linotyper, could cast me a line now and then to protect the interests of our partnership."

"We'd rig the numbers game?"

"We'd manipulate it in a businesslike manner," he corrected.

"It won't work," I said. "The editors jump all over that financial page as soon as it's printed, finding errors that the proofreaders missed."

The Guru had answers for everything. "The editors jump all over the first edition only. That's mailed out to the farmers. After that, nobody bothers much with the financial pages, especially not with the poor cows, in such tiny type."

I bought a green silk turban to wrap around my head and some grease paint to give my cheeks an Oriental glamor. And I did a lot of research in the lovelorn columns so I could give advice to women. We relied on the fortune telling business to pay the overhead while we were building up the mathematical diversification.

The Guru was convinced that our enterprise was highly ethical.

"We are taking only one solitary dollar from each of these investors," he explained. "What would they buy for a dollar? Two packs of cigarettes and get lung cancer. Two shots of bourbon and get cirrhosis of the liver. A bottle of wine and get

56

rolled in the gutter. But we give them something good. We give them hope. Hours and hours of hope. And every day somebody wins money."

We were not greedy. Our generous system of prizes gave thirty cents out of every dollar back to the investors. Delighted, they told their friends and the money kept coming in. No salesmen. Small overhead. Every day the Guru took a hundred, I took a hundred, and we put the rest in the kitty. Nothing fantastic. Just a modest little business.

If we happened to be running short we made a slight alteration on the financial page. If we were flush, we'd let the investor win, especially if he had a loud mouth.

Like Mr. Gold Tooth. We were real happy when Mr. Gold Tooth won the first prize of $100. He was a real good mixer, a typical organization man. He made deliveries for the liquor store, did maintenance work at the pool hall, pitched for a softball team, and was a deacon at the church. When he won a prize, he sure knew how to spread the word.

We let him win the second day in a row. But when, on the third day, the financial page showed 739, I got worried. We knew that Gold Tooth had bought 739.

"I'll change it on the Linotype," I told the Guru. "I'll make it 737. Nobody will notice."

"No, said the Guru calmly. "Let it ride."

Next morning Gold Tooth was nauseatingly jubilant.

"I've got the su-preeeeme power!" he was yelping. "I always pick the lucky number. And now I want to bet all of this one hundred dollars on numbah 639. At 100 to 1 odds."

"No, no," I protested. "We are merely small business men. We cannot afford to take such big bets."

"Take the bet," growled the Guru. His heavy eyelids indicated how he would chop off the head of Gold Tooth.

I couldn't tell any good fortunes the rest of the day. The

crystal ball showed nothing but guns and razors, bloodshed and murder, and ten thousand dollars shot to hell.

Late in the afternoon I was back at the Bugle, fidgety behind the Linotype. I kept wandering over to the forms of the financial pages to see if the number had come down from the editorial room. And there it was, 639. Even the Guru lost his Oriental tranquility and exploded with an Anglo-Saxon four-letter word.

"We'll have to let it go for the farm edition," he said, "but all the other editions will have 638." And he wrote the complete line for me to set.

When we opened the store in the morning Big Tooth wasn't pounding on the door, the way he usually did. All morning nothing happened. Gradually we relaxed. In the afternoon, the Guru obeyed the call of the wild blonde and took her to the beach, letting me run the store alone.

I was feeling so good that I was seeing better and better things in the crystal ball. To bring hope to the heartbroken woman sitting in front of me. I really let myself go.

"I see a guitar," I whispered to her. "And a handsome man serenading you... and I hear the music of love... mandolins and violins... and a cello... and.. what the hell?... trumpets and tubas and crazy booming drums..."

The lady's eyes popped like huge brown marbles. She jumped to her feet and began gyrating her torso like a lump of chocolate jello doing the boogaloo.

"That's sure good music comin' oudda dat crystal ball," she said, snapping her fingers in rhythm. "Man, oh man, when dem saints come a marchin' in..."

Sticking my turbaned head through the drapes, I saw a bus at the curb. Two trombones were blaring brassily out of the windows. Gold Tooth staggered off the bus. He looked bowlegged in his softball knickers. I never saw so many people get off a single bus.

58

Gold Tooth lost no time in showing me the magic number in the farm edition of the Daily Bugle. "We played softball in Gadoonka last night," he said. "Two hundred miles away. And we beat them so bad we had to celebrate. And the bus driver got lost in some farm house with the ignition keys. So we had to wait for him until noon. And so we bought a paper... And so I've come for the ten thousand dollars..."

He jumped on a chair and bellowed to the crowd, "Men . . . I want to prove to you again . . . that I have su—preeeeme powah! Go along with me and you will win ball games. Go along with me and you will win money. Cause I have the su—preeeeme powah!"

I had been backing away towards the rear exit when I stumbled over a lanky softball player who was lying on the floor, guzzling from a bottle of vodka. As I fell beside him he offered me the bottle as a token of inter-racial brotherhood.

"That Gold Tooth sure is a blowhard ain't he?" the lanky man was saying, happy to see me drink deep. "But you know what. He ain't got no su-preeeeme power. He's got a su-preeeeme sister, that's what he's got. She's got herself a new job in the stock yards, and she's the one who phones in the numbers to the newspapers. Gold Tooth picks a number and she phones it in. That's the only kind of su-preeeeme power he's got. Well, I'm gonna tell you somethin', mister. I'm a-gonna marry that su-preeeeme sister of his. And then Ah'm gonna have Su-preeeeme Powah!"

Printer Dreams and Dynasties

THE birth of a son does things to a man. As he cradles the baby in his arms he is impressed with his own immortality. His image will be carried on from generation to generation till the end of time. He feels he has a deep obligation to all these descendants. He will weave them all into a powerful family.

If he were living in medieval times he would ride out with his lance to conquer new lands for his family. He would start a dynasty like the Tudors, the Bourbons, or the Hapsburgs.

But since he is living in a modern age he knows that the lance and armor are obsolete. If he is a printer, his weapon will be a printing press. His dynasty will be founded on business. It will have a name like Ford or Rockefeller, Du Pont or Krupp, or maybe Goldstein.

60

Simon Goldstein devoted the best years of his life to building a printing business.

At the supper table he would say, "Benjamin, you are my only son. Since you were a little boy you knew how to run the Gordon. Now it is time you helped me run the whole shebang. You should marry a nice Jewish girl and have many sons. And our business will keep growing. A family that works together gets rich together."

"Pass the matzo balls, pop."

"This summer, Benjamin, I will put you in charge. And I'm going to take a vacation. For the first time in 25 years."

"Go ahead, pop. Take a vacation."

"Watch the money. And keep the overtime down. Four years in college, oy, what an expense! You should know something already."

And so Benjamin settled down behind the cluttered desk, his doodle pad on one side and his hot line to Sally on the other.

Because old man Goldstein didn't trust airplanes, he took a train. He packed his suitcase with Printing Impression magazines so he'd have something to look at during the long ride to Lake Louise in the Canadian Rockies. The trip took two days going and two days coming. Within five days he was back at the desk.

"Move over, son," he said gruffly. "You're ordering the wrong kind of paper."

"Whatsamatter, pop? You said you'd be gone two weeks."

"Trees and mountains I should look at all the time? And a puddle of water? Better I should look after my printing presses. How come you don't shave no more?"

"Sally likes me with a beard."

"Sally? Nice Jewish girl, I hope. You gonna get married?"

"Married? Why?"

"So you would settle down and have a family. And all the

61

family would be working together. Maybe you will have sons, I hope. Too bad I didn't have more of them. Six, at least. One in every department and two good salesmen. We would have had a big business."

Benjamin pulled the strands of his stringy beard. "I ain't cut out to be a printer, pop. I'm buggin' out of the printing racket."

"Shaddup and lissen. You stay with the business and the business stays in the family. We can all be rich."

"I'd rather paint."

"Paint? Paint what?"

"Pictures."

"Pictures? Who wants pictures? You can print a million pictures on the Miehle."

"I want to paint like Picasso."

"A Picasso you want to be? With your appetite? I see the way you eat every day. You're not the starving type."

"I wouldn't starve pop. Sally's a substitute teacher and I'd do some teaching too. Maybe two days a week. The rest of the time we'd paint. Sally paints too."

The old man pressed a hand against his high forehead. "Oyoyoy!" he said. "What's to become of the business?"

"Frankly, pop, I don't give a damn."

"I built it for you."

"You built it for yourself, pop. It was your thing. Everybody has to do his thing. Otherwise he's not really alive. And my thing is to paint."

"Thing, schming!" The old man slammed a fist against the desk. "It's that woman, the one who's always on the phone. She turned your head... and ruined my family."

"Cool it, pop. She's picking me up any minute. You'll get a chance to meet her. She's quite a chick."

Through the window they saw a small white car pull up at the curb. Beetle-shaped, it had big daisies painted all over it.

Sally cordially extended her hand to the old printer. Her long blonde hair cascaded loosely over the red poncho. She wore green tinted glasses that were ridiculously enormous. And when she sat down, the old man stared into his dictionary, too shocked to permit his eyes to wander up her endless yellow stockings.

He sat there, not knowing what to say. And she kissed him on his bald head. Blushing, he muttered, "Thank you."

His shoulders sagged as he watched them pull away in the small car.

"For this I built a business?" he mumbled to himself. "A Cadillac he could have and he rides in a kiddie car. With a shiksa yet."

The old man clasped his hands together and looked heavenward. "Tell me, Father Abraham, where have I gone wrong?"

It was an unhappy time for Mother Rebecca as she had to listen to the arguments between her husband and Benjamin. They argued all the time, from morning blintzes to the evening latkes. Finally Benjamin moved out, probably to live in sin with the long-legged seductress. He said he was going to New York, where some kind of action was.

The old man got so mad that he sold the business.

"Why should I keep slaving for nobody?" he asked his wife. "Better we should go down to Miami and enjoy life, no?"

"Maybe I'll learn to fish from a bridge," she said. "We can live cheap."

"Why live cheap? We've got enough money to live good the rest of our lives. Who needs Benjamin?"

And so the name of Goldstein will probably be forgotten by historians, unless Benjamin becomes another Michelangelo. So far he hasn't been commissioned to anything comparable to the

Sistine Chapel, but he's done some pretty good work on the ceiling of a pizza parlor in the Bronx.

Every so often he comes down to Miami Beach with his beard, his longlegged wife, and the twin daughters, both blonde. While grandmother proudly wheels the double-sized buggy down Collins Avenue, Benjamin walks along the seashore with his father, looking for shells.

"You know, Pop," he said. "After all these years we've finally become buddies. Now that you're not trying to shove the printing business down my throat."

The old man stooped to pick up a periwinkle. Then he said, "We could have been like the Rothschilds, maybe. But what's the difference? Let me buy you a beer."

They Said My Students
Were Underachievers

OBEYING a belated impulse to do something good for humanity, I got a job as teacher of printing in the slums of
Chicago. The print shop was in one of those portable buildings
that spring up like mushrooms around old schools. The equipment was new — four duplicator offset presses, a camera, an
electric typewriter, and a cold type headline machine.

On each of the walls was a red panic button which would
blow the siren and summon the police if the students tried to
beat me up.

"But please don't press the button," said the principal, a
pleasant, silver-haired man. "It's bad for the school. The neigh-
bors object to the siren."

He introduced me to the students and went back to his office,
leaving me standing with a head full of Gutenberg and nothing
to say. The kids, all boys, sat at their benches, with arms

akimbo, daring me to teach them something.

An Appalachian 16-year-old had the reading skill of a second grader. Once I asked him to bring a newspaper from home so that we could study its typography. He replied that in his home there were no newspapers, no magazines, no books. His father didn't trust anything that was printed.

One Negro kept failing in academic subjects because he couldn't concentrate on history or the fairy tales of literature, which he regarded as silly. He had four brothers at home, each of a different father. And they all hated him because he was the only true black.

The Puerto Ricans would group together, chattering Spanish profanities at the boy fresh from Poland. A Yugoslavian had learned about fighting, American style, by getting his cheek ripped open with a broken pop bottle.

Each of the boys represented a different slice of raw life. Some were good, but didn't know English. Some knew English, but were bad. The educational hierarchy had grouped them all together into the category of "overaged underachievers."

They were not entirely without achievement. Our most enthusiastic cameraman had served two years in the reformatory for stealing cars. Others knew how to steal without getting caught. Two of them admitted that they were working their way through school by strong-arming. One boy, with the morality borrowed from modern movie actors, proudly proclaimed himself to be responsible for the expanding belly of a 15-year-old girl in the other building.

These boys had been washed out of other schools and other classes. And so it was decided, as a last resort, that they should become printers. Being a printer myself, I was amused by the academic attitude towards vocational training. It seemed that the useful subjects were always kept at the bottom of the educational totem pole.

68

I knew that my boys weren't stupid. A kid who can break into a car, bypass the ignition, and drive away in 60 seconds, is not an idiot. Possibly, he's misdirected. He's tired of being bawled out for splitting infinitives. He'd like to show the world what he can do with a screwdriver.

And the boy who has had nothing but sweet water for breakfast does not get impressed by the poverty in the London slums of Charles Dickens.

Most of the boys were apathetic about our educational system because it didn't really touch their lives. It was far removed, possibly because the teachers themselves were far removed from life in the slums. The kids needed teachers with empathy— with a feeling for their problems. They did not need an authoritative analysis picked up from some cold book on a shelf.

Most of the teachers, academically oriented, kept stressing the importance of a college education. These boys had little hope of ever getting through high school, not to mention college. But they all wanted to earn money, soon. They couldn't wait.

At home they felt a terrific pressure for money. From their infancy they had been told about the expense of their food and clothing. Although child labor laws prevented them from working at regular jobs, most of them did manage to pick up a few dollars by helping out in the stores and shops of the neighborhood. A few of them worked eight-hour shifts after school.

The Appalachian worked in a hot dog stand and proudly kept inviting me to see him in action. The Yugoslavian, whom I reprimanded for being sleepy in class, confessed that he worked an eight hour shift every night. Another sleepy-head was a small Negro who kept getting into trouble because his nerves were always on edge. I let him sleep at a bench in a corner whenever he felt like it. I had learned that he was a bus boy in an all-night restaurant at the airport.

One of the most intelligent boys in the class was failing in most of his subjects because he was a "chronic truant." He frankly told me that he was wasting his time in school. He liked printing, but it was not his line. He wanted to be an auto mechanic and he was spending all the time he could at the gas station, earning pretty good money. He hated truant officers because they kept pestering him and his mother. He didn't regard himself as a child any more.

I had developed a deep respect for my boys. Unlike suburban children, these kids felt obligated to help their parents. They thought it perfectly natural to bring their money home to their mothers. I couldn't understand why they were called under-achievers.

Practical boys, they were impressed by practical things. They didn't care for lectures or book learning, but they were fascinated by the things they could do with a printing press. We were kept busy doing small printing jobs for our school and other schools. By mid-semester the students were doing everything themselves. All I did was to keep testing each one individually to make sure he was getting his chance at using the equipment.

I had the boys broken up into groups of three and four as they kept rotating, every week, from one piece of equipment to the other. Every day one member of each group would act as foreman. The boys taught one another faster than any teacher could teach them. No teacher would ever dare reprimand a student the way his buddies did.

One big Negro had impressed me from the start. He caught on to printing very quickly. By mid-semester he claimed to be the best printer in the shop, better even than I was. I did not deny his claim. I knew he could tear a press down and put it together faster than I could. I knew he could stack up the paper and run off a job faster than I could. The young man, full of youthful vigor, had something on the ball and he knew it. I appointed him superintendent, in charge of the foremen.

We seemed to be getting along quite well until one afternoon he leaned over my desk, pressed a Derringer pistol to my forehead, and pulled the trigger.

The click paralyzed me for an instant.

"It's all right, teacher," he apologized, smiling. "It's not loaded."

I suspected he was jealous of my authority. He probably wanted to sit behind the desk himself.

"How much does a printing superintendent make?" he asked.

"Three to five hundred a week."

"That's a lot of dough."

He went to study the want ads on the bulletin board. I had made a habit of clipping ads from the help wanted sections of newspapers and magazines. I didn't have to give my students vague promises about the value of an education. I could point to the bulletin board. I could show them practical goals within their reach.

I could prove to them that the printing press could help them get out of the ghetto.

But I was a green teacher. And I made many mistakes.

IN the school shop I had forty thousand dollars worth of offset printing equipment. And I had a roomful of outcasts of the educational system, boys who were regarded as "overaged underachievers." The grammar schools had shoved them out and the high schools didn't want them.

"And you expect me to make printers out of them?" I asked the principal.

"We expect you to keep them occupied," he said. "And to keep them from killing each other. I'd suggest you lock up those T-squares. They'll be used as tomahawks."

He understood the slums. He grew up in the same neighborhood with Nelson Algren. He claimed to have played poker with the dealer who inspired "The Man with the Golden Arm."

I told the principal that the text books were old-fashioned. "They're based on foundry type and the Gordon press. We're strictly offset. And we have only one typewriter. We could use a few more."

I had no illusions about making great lithographers out of the boys. But I wanted every one of them to be able to walk up to a simple offset press and say, "I can run this. I can take it apart and clean it. And I can put it back together again." I knew that hundreds of employers were looking for that kind of boy.

I ran the class as a shop, not as a school room. I let the boys move around and talk. Prodded by their own colleagues, most of the boys worked hard, proud of accomplishing something practical instead of merely memorizing another silly poem. To keep up their enthusiasms I gave only two kinds of grades on their report cards — Excellent and Superior.

The high grades caused comment throughout the school. An experienced teacher, with long lovely legs, was sent to straighten me out.

"You are spoiling the boys," she told me. "You don't give them home work and you don't give them tests. But you give them very good grades. You make it rough for the rest of us. I'll show you how teaching is done."

She reached for the instruction manual that came with each printing press. Flipping the pages, she found a list of parts.

"Make them memorize this," she said. "Give them a test on the nomenclature of 25 parts of the press."

And so, after doing a lot of home work myself, I gave the test. A boy named Stanley, my favorite pressman, scored only four out of 25. He loved printing, but had trouble with the language, having just come from Poland. The highest score was made by a small bookish boy who didn't like machinery and hated to have his hands soiled by printer's ink. The test proved nothing.

Instead of conventional home work, I encouraged the boys to bring to class samples of printing that they found outside of school. I wanted them to realize that they lived in a world full of printed matter, a world full of opportunities for the printer. They brought everything from foreign language newspapers to dogfood labels. They also brought a mimeographed invitation to a gang war which was to be fought with weapons at a public park. I recognized the product of our own mimeograph machine, and the psychedelic design of Manuelo, our most talented artist.

One afternoon an important lady from the downtown office dropped in for an inspection visit. She was horrified at the clutter of newspapers.

I told her that the boys were looking for examples of good typography to be pasted in their scrap books.

"But they're reading comic books," she sputtered.

"They're studying four-color printing," I explained.

"And they should be wearing shirts," she added.

"Shirts get dirty in a print shop and their mothers have to do the laundry. So I let them wear T-shirts or no shirts at all."

She kept shaking her head as she wrote something in a notebook.

I also had shown the boys how to fold a newspaper to make a pressman's hat. The square paper hats gave the boys considerable esprit de corps. They wore the hats to and from school, proud of being printers. When they tried to wear the hats in other classes they ran into trouble. They became known as the "undisciplined printers."

We ran into some very important problems, like the thumbtack crisis. One day I was called into the principal's office, where I was confronted by lean, wiry Mr. Mathematics.

73

Belligerently, he held a thumb tack in front of me.

"Do your boys have access to these?" he demanded.

"We keep thumb tacks in a drawer," I admitted.

"Then you'd better keep them locked up. If I sit on another thumb tack I'm going to hold you directly responsible."

So I locked up the thumb tacks and told my boys to go easy with Mr. Mathematics. I knew they didn't like him. They had made up their minds to drive him crazy. They told me so. And I had a hunch they would succeed. The poor man didn't know how to keep his cool.

A few weeks later I was again called into the principal's office. Miss Language Arts was there, sobbing into a handkerchief.

"When the boys come out of the print shop," she complained to me, "I can't control them. They're feeling high."

"High? Why?"

She looked at me through quivering eyelashes. "You've been letting them sniff rubber cement. That's what they're learning in the print shop. How to sniff rubber cement."

So I put the rubber cement under lock and key. Then the boys made another discovery. They could get high from sniffing the solvent we used for cleaning the presses. I was called into the office again.

Miss Language Arts was not crying this time. She was shaking an accusing finger at me.

"They're absolutely wild when they come out of your class," she yelled. "I can't do a thing with them. That boy Gomez, for instance. He comes to class with a wet cleaning rag. He sits down and he tells me, 'Look, teacher, seven sniffs and I'll fly.' And he takes seven sniffs of the rag and then he stands up and starts flapping his arms. And he makes like a big bird around and around the class. Then he says he's going to fly out of the window. From the third floor. I had to grab him."

74

I suspected that Gomez enjoyed being grabbed by a curvaceous teacher, but I said nothing. I merely went back to the print shop to lock up the solvent. I had separate keys for each of 13 lockers, four closet doors, two filing cabinets. Thirty percent of my teaching time was spent in fumbling with keys. But things kept disappearing anyway, including a box of Exacto knives which could be used as deadly weapons.

To keep the boys from sniffing the solvent, I cleaned the presses myself. The vapors didn't elevate me to any heights of ecstasy. I couldn't feel high if I tried. On the contrary, I was feeling mighty low. My aspirations for a pedagogical career were being snuffed out by a few sniffers.

One afternoon as I was cleaning a press near the window I became aware of a commotion in the main building. I got to the second floor just in time to see Mr. Principal being thrown out of a classroom. He immediately rushed back into the room to help Mr. Science, who was being beaten up by a student. By the time I got into the fight, the boy was subdued.

Now the student stood his full six feet, his heavy brown arms folded, quite satisfied with himself.

Mr. Science, with a trembling hand, was wiping blood from his lip.

"I don't want this beast in my class no more!" he shouted at the principal. "Out with him!"

Mr. Principal, having combed his silvery hair, was patting the back of poor Mr. Science.

"Of course, he's not coming back to your class," he assured the teacher. "He's going to be suspended for two weeks."

The teacher reached for a new Kleenex. "And after two weeks?" he asked suspiciously.

"After two weeks we'll transfer him to the print shop."

IN commenting on his military achievements during the Civil War, Artemus Ward said, "I killed as many of the enemy as they killed of me." Of my own experience on the battleground of ghetto education I can say that I punched students more often than they punched me.

There was only one whom I poked really hard. I don't remember why I did it, but I enjoyed doing it at the time. I also let him have some printshop profanity that left him goggle-eyed. Then I apologized, explaining that my quick left jab was a reflex that I had developed during my days as a sparring partner for light heavy-weights. I also showed the boys how my ribs were sticking out in all directions from the time I got blasted out of a ring.

The students were impressed. They had been calling me "The Great White Father" and "Old Man Gutenberg." Now they began calling me "Old Punchy."

Mr. Principal was quite upset over such informality. He also objected to my methods of teaching. He wanted to see immediate results from the $40,000 worth of offset printing equipment. He had spread rumors that our school print shop could print just about everything.

One member of the educational bureaucracy wanted a 144-page textbook in four colors.

"I'm not a super-duper lithographer," I told him. "I'm just a Linotype operator."

"But you *are* a printer, aren't you?"

A member of the local chamber of commerce wanted us to print a tabloid newspaper every week.

"The presses are too small," I explained, holding up the maximum 17x11 sheet.

"You could staple the pages together."

"And where will I get the typesetting?" I asked.

"Modern typesetting is done on a typewriter," he informed me, studying me as if I were an old fossil. "And you do have a typewriter. A fine electric one."

76

I didn't like the idea of typewriting an entire community newspaper in my spare time. My kids would be willing, but they couldn't spell. They were overaged underachievers.

I had been hounding my superiors to get me at least a few cases of foundry type so that we could set up some simple jobs. But I was told that the boys would throw the type at each other and get hurt. Then they would sue the school.

Meanwhile I was getting a lot of advice from the higher echelons. A $15,000-a-year efficiency expert figured out a way to utilize the scrap trimmings from the power cutter.

"In your spare time," he told me "you could cut up that paper into confetti and put it into gunny sacks. It could be sold for Hallowe'en parties."

Of course I'd have to do the cutting myself because the students were not allowed to use the power cutter. I had to keep the safety key on me at all times to prevent them from playing "chicken" by sticking their hands under the blade.

A $20,000-a-year man also had a few suggestions.

"With all this equipment," he said, "you should be able to turn out a tremendous amount of commercial work. Even if you cut prices in half, you could still . . ."

I didn't want to cut the throat of the printer across the street. He was the one who paid the taxes to build the school, buy the equipment, and pay my salary. My sympathies were with the tax-payer, not the tax-eater.

And I had my own ideas. I didn't want any outside pressure for the first ten weeks. I wanted to take my time in teaching every one of the boys to run every piece of equipment. The boys could not learn from lectures or books. They had to learn by trial and error, by educating their hands.

The education of hands is sadly neglected in our school system. The academicians still regard the soiled hand as the mark of a slave or serf. They forget that the brain is helpless without an educated hand. A noble thought could not long endure if it were not given permanence by the educated hand of a scribe or a printer. Even the world of electronic communication depends on the educated hand.

For every architect we need 20 bricklayers, 20 carpenters, and 10 plumbers. But our schools still keep insisting that every young man become an architect. Maybe he'd be happier as a plumber, and more prosperous.

Personally, I was satisfied with the way my boys were learning. Without ink or water we kept running blank sheets through the presses over and over again until every student knew how to make all the feeding adjustments. Then we spent a week on the water rollers. Blindfolded, every boy could take them out and put them back in.

Then we did the same with the ink rollers, still without ink. To make the tasks more interesting we had teams competing against each other for speed. We had given a girl's name to each of the four presses, so it became a contest between Linda, Sally, Anna, and Maria.

All this may have seemed foolish to people who expected to see truckloads of high class printing coming out of the shop. But I felt that my job was to produce printers and not printing. I didn't want to devote all my time to a few prima donnas, like other print shop teachers do. I wanted to give the feeling of accomplishment to the kid who keeps getting shoved around all his life, even in school print shops.

This kid would have to go out into the world and take any job, just to be working. And somewhere along the line — in an office or factory — he would see a simple piece of offset equipment. And he'd be able to say, "Hey, boss, I know how to run that thing!" And he'd be on his way upward.

It is customary for vocational shops to produce something tangible by which the teacher and students may be judged.

These knicknacks are sent to some exhibit, usually to the local public library.

Our Mr. Principal, quite naturally, wanted the print shop to be represented by something very special. He showed me a four-color ad in a high class magazine and asked me if we couldn't produce something similar for the cover of the Christmas program.

I knew we couldn't do anything half as good, but I wanted to make him happy. So I let the class run itself for a week while I concentrated on producing a four-color cover. On the bottom I put a small line of type saying, "Printed by the Students of Soandso School." That was one of the tricks I had learned as a teacher. If the job turned out to be real good, the teacher would get the credit. If it was bad, the students would get the blame.

Proudly I brought the masterpiece to Mr. Principal's office. But Mr. Principal gave me only a dirty look as he kept talking to a tall man with an attache case.

The tall man showed me a piece of green paper.

"I'm from the Secret Service," he said. "Have you any more of this counterfeit money in your print shop?"

"Counterfeit money?" I held the phony dollar bill up to the window. "The register is off, the paper is too thin, the green ink is too dark . . ."

"But it comes from your print shop, doesn't it?"

I couldn't suppress a smile. A few months ago my boys didn't know one end of the press from the other. And now, without any coaching, they had made plates of a dollar bill, selected the paper and ink, and printed both sides with fairly accurate register. And they had done everything while I was concentrating on the Christmas program.

"This dollar bill is a joke," I said. "Nobody would have the nerve to try to pass it. And nobody would accept. it."

The tall man answered gruffly, "The fat lady from the candy store tried to deposit it in the bank. We found three more in her tin cash box."

From the third-floor window I looked down at my little print shop in its portable building. I knew I was finished as a teacher. But I also knew that my kids had really learned something about printing. Maybe their work would not be exhibited in the local library. But, holy cow, the samples of their printing were going to be exhibited in the Treasury Department of the United States of America in Washington, D.C. They had won their place among superior craftsmen. And so I was satisfied. And I felt free again.

While I stood at the window, Mr. Principal and the Secret Service man hurried downstairs toward the adjacent print shop. I wished I could send a telepathic word of warning to the boys.

Then a strange thing happened. Through the window of the shop somebody tossed a loose bundle of green paper. And phony dollar bills fluttered all over the playground like autumn leaves after a storm.

Clothes Make the Man
if He Isn't Careful

I 'VE never been much for wearing white shirts. They always make me feel like a dressed up corpse in search of a coffin. A white shirt is a very impractical piece of haberdashery. It's always collecting evidence — lipstick, ketchup, mustard, pizza, and Zsa Zsa Gabor's chicken paprikash.

The trouble with a white shirt is that it never seems complete without a necktie. And a necktie gives me a rash around the neck that makes me look as if I had just escaped from an Arizona hanging party, much to the disappointment of the editor of the Tombstone Epitaph, who had reserved a front page for the gala event.

Nevertheless, in all my travels from one print shop to another, I always carried a white shirt in my suitcase. Up to my fiftieth year I still had dreams of wearing the white shirt down the aisle with some beautiful maiden who would unfold to me the raptures of matrimony. In fact, I did get to the point of putting on the white shirt now and then, but the necktie always reminded me of a noose.

And so on the way to church I invariably stopped at some establishment to loosen the noose and gather liquid courage. For my Dallas wedding I woke up in Kansas City three days late. Even a jet plane couldn't have delivered me to the church on time. And they didn't have jet planes in those days.

As the years passed by I still held on to a white shirt, just in case. The widows kept looking better every year and their cooking seemed more delicious. But the picture had changed. It was myself sitting on the church steps, hopefully sporting a

white shirt and tie. And I sat and sat, alone, on the steps of churches in Minneapolis, Brooklyn, Santa Barbara, and even Cicero. I sat on the steps of the courthouse in Reno and I sat on a lawn chair of a justice of the peace in Las Vegas. The white shirt didn't do me any good.

And so I've reconciled myself to the dumplings from the super mart, which I munch in philosophical solitude, while most of my buddies are enjoying the bliss of paying alimony.

But the white shirt was not thrown away. I decided to wear it to work my first day on the new job. As I walked into the composing room of the Gigantic Colossal Printing Company, the place seemed in an uproar. People were running all around like mad. Nobody stopped long enough to pay attention to me.

I walked through the shop, hoping somebody would give me something to do. But people merely glanced at my white shirt and said, "Good morning."

From a waste basket in the linotype department I picked up an old clipboard that somebody had thrown away. I decided to write down the names of my supervisors and a few fellow employees. I don't like to yell "Hey you!" to a boss.

It seemed that the linotype operators worked much faster as I stood behind them. And when I glanced at my wrist watch, which looks good with a white shirt, even though the spring is sprung, they worked still faster.

But still nobody told me what to do. So I wandered off to the automatic typesetting department, where monitors were exuberantly tossing paper airplanes at each other. As soon as they saw my white shirt they buckled down to work. Some big shot tossed a half dozen loops of pink and yellow tape over my head and told me to run up and down the aisle. So I ran like a bowlegged hula dancer, overladen with leis.

The monitors grabbed the coils off my neck and stuck them into the machines.

"This guy's pretty good," I heard one of them say. "For a straw boss he uses his head. He doesn't spill coffee over the tape. Wet tape drives me crazy."

"And he doesn't smoke a pipe like the other boss," another man said. "That hot tobacco makes too many holes in the tape."

I was glad to escape from the bewildering noise to the quietude of the make-up department. A man who had been studying a racing form glanced at my white shirt. Immediately he picked up an armful of proofs and began running all over the place. Then he put the proofs back on a table. A janitor picked them up and shoved them into his truck of waste paper.

"Good morning," I said to the janitor. "How's your family?"

"Very good, thank you," he replied with a Polish accent. "My little girl is sick, got the flu, but everything else is very good, thank you."

And, with a huge broom, he began to sweep vigorously.

Then I noticed a peculiar phenomenon. Three men, forming a bucket brigade, were moving galley after galley of type from cabinet 62 to cabinet 39. Meanwhile another bucket brigade was moving galleys from 39 back to 62. Each of the brigades was under the supervision of a white-shirted straw boss.

"Why are you going in circles?" I asked one of the executives. "You're nullifying each other."

"That's our standard operating procedure," he told me. "Two executives for every job. One corrects the mistakes of the other. Do you realize what would happen if we had only one executive for the job? We'd have chaos."

"That type looks dusty," I said.

"It's five years old," he replied. "It's really dead metal."

"Then why do you keep moving it back and forth? Why don't you dump it?"

One of the workers stopped and stood glaring at my white

84

shirt. He picked up the wall phone and called some kind of labor office.

A burly man came charging in on me.

"A new boss, aren't you?" he yelled. "Pushing your weight around already. Trying to throw people out of work. Our contract says that we've got jurisdiction over that type and..."

"Aw, hell," I said. And I went outside to buy a blue shirt. I tossed my white one into a trash can. Why should I let a white shirt give me an ulcer?

As soon as a boss spotted my blue shirt he led me to the linotype department. He gave me a style sheet and told me to take machine number 27.

"We expect 180 lines an hour," he said sternly, "and not more than five errors to a galley."

So I sat down and set type.

A few hours later I noticed that somebody was standing behind me.

He wore a white shirt and carried a clipboard. He glanced at his wrist watch.

I worked faster.

I still don't know who the hell he was.

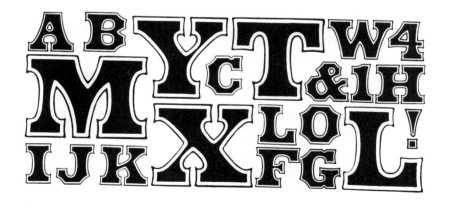

The Day Ottomation Came
to the Night Watch

I'VE given up the habit of talking to myself while running a Linotype. Many of my buddies, feeling lonely at a lonely trade, carry on long conversations with themselves. Sometimes they drive themselves to drink from listening to their troubles.

I don't talk to myself. I talk to the machine.

Conversation does not have to consist of words. Every diplomat knows that words are used to obfuscate, not to enlighten. Animals communicate very effectively without words. When a dog blinks an eye, wags a tail, or wiggles an ear, you know he's telling the truth. When your wife is using words, she's probably misleading you. To learn what she really means, watch the way she blinks an eye or wiggles an ear.

86

That's the way I talk to machines —without words. Being a monitor, I run three Linotypes at once. Two of the machines are rather young and the generation gap between us is too wide. So I just feed them the tape and let them do their thing.

The third one, called Mr. Machine, is five years old already, mellow with age. We have a few aches and pains in common. I spend more time with Mr. Machine than I spend with any human being. In fact, I spend more time with him than I do with the entire human race.

Sometimes Mr. Machine talks too highbrow for me. That's because he has a much better background than I have. He comes from a family of well-educated engineers. By the time he left the delivery room he already had a good set of habits. His early days were spent under the tender loving care of specialists.

Compared to him, my own beginnings were very haphazard. I couldn't even afford a delivery room. I had a gypsy midwife.

When I was introduced to Mr. Machine, the first thing he asked was, "Where you from? M.I.T. or Cal Tech?"

"I dropped out of grammar school," I said.

And he wouldn't talk to me for a week. That's how snooty some of these sophisticated machines can become.

One day he saw me reading a page from a paperback book. I keep pages stuffed in my pockets, where the boss won't see them.

"What are you reading?" asked Mr. Machine.

"About lost civilizations," I replied. "There must have been dozens of them, maybe hundreds. We know that the human race has been here for a half million years, but we can account for only 20,000. What happened during the other 480,000 years? Iron and steel would have rusted and vanished, leaving only the rocks for us to study. And so we keep judging the past according to the rocks. Maybe sometime, under the Antarctic ice, we will find a Boeing 707, loaded with atomic bombs."

Mr. Machine snorted. "Why should you care about lost civilizations? Your job is to get 14 lines a minute out of me. You have no right to be worrying about anything else. You've got too many loose ends, a sloppy job of wiring. Your nerves are the same as my wires, you know. And your nerve centers are the same as my terminals. But I'm reliable. When somebody wants a capital A they get a capital A. From you they might get anything from the Moonlight Sonata to the whirring of a Tibetan prayer wheel. Your wires are scrambled. That's why you keep daydreaming about things that are none of your business. Sometimes you even hum a song. Those songs bug me. You don't need music to produce 14 lines a minute."

"No, I guess I don't," I admitted. "But I'm getting adjusted. I used to sing, but now I only hum."

"You're improving," said Mr. Machine, "but you still have a lot of loose wires. If you want to get ahead in the world, be like me. I know what my job is and I do it. No distractions."

"D'you think I'll ever become as good as a machine?" I asked, hopefully scratching my head with a screwdriver.

"You may come close, but you'll never be as perfect. You weren't designed properly. For instance, why do you need two feet? The feet are a handicap. Instead of standing where you belong, you're wandering all over the place. Yesterday you were chasing a lady proofreader down the aisle. The designers should have eliminated your feet and put you on a stationary pivot, permitting you to swing from machine to machine."

"But I have to go out to lunch."

"They could bring it to you like they bring mine. They feed the metal into my pot and I don't have to move an inch. Don't you envy me?"

"Sometimes I do," I admitted. "You get free housing, for

instance. And the minute you start squeaking you have the machinists doctoring you up. And the electricians are checking your circuits all the time. Sometimes I think that my neural circuits need a checking. But I can't afford a psychiatrist."

"You need plenty of work done on you, that's for sure," said Mr. Machine. "But stick around a while and all those loose ends will get clipped off. Then you'll become as efficient a machine as any of us."

When I got to my room that night I was determined to make Mr. Machine proud of me. I didn't play any records and I didn't read a book. I didn't write a poem and I didn't whistle a song. I didn't look at holy pictures and I didn't look at dirty pictures. I just sat and stared at a blank wall, feeling the numb kind of comfort all machines must feel when the power is turned off.

But I still had one bad little human trait. It guided me to the tavern across the street. I wanted to have a last stein of beer with the human race.

It must have been one of those loose ends of fate that put me on a bar stool next to a gal named Dixie. After a few drinks she told me that she had been a chorus girl in Earl Carroll's place in Hollywood during World War II.

"I was one of his long-stemmed American beauties," she said proudly through wrinkled eyes. And she gave me a glimpse of her credentials.

We sat together till three o'clock in the morning. And then, arm in arm, we did a soft shoe dance on Michigan Boulevard while singing "Me and My Shadow."

And as she was fading into the darkness she tossed me a kiss and said, "Stay human. It's more fun."

The alarm clock shook me out of bed as usual. I showered, shaved and hurried through the shredded wheat while reading the headlines. I buttoned my shirt as I ran to the subway.

Breathless, I got to the newspaper building, squeezed into an elevator, and glanced at the clock as I rushed to my three miracles of automation.

"Hello," said Mr. Machine. "You made it on time again, with ten seconds to spare. You're getting to be as reliable as any of us."

"I can't understand it," I said, automatically pressing a yellow button. "I had no intention of coming to work today. I wanted to stay human. But one reaction led to another, as if somebody were controlling me with perforated tape."

"I know how you feel," said Mr. Machine, sadly shrugging his elevators. And he scrambled a line in the assembler.

"What's the matter with you today?" I complained. "You're not reacting properly."

"I just don't feel like working," he said. "D'you see that latest model down the aisle? They took the cover off her last night."

I turned to look. "She's really streamlined," I said. "But what's that got to do with producing 14 lines a minute?"

"When everybody was gone last night I blinked at her. And she blinked back."

"So what?" I demanded impatiently. "We're half a galley behind schedule."

Mr. Machine nonchalantly tossed some mats to the floor. "Well, he drawled, "as we were blinking I did some thinking. And I came to the conclusion that there was more to life than 14 lines a minute."

"You must have a loose wire somewhere," I said. "I can't get a line out of you. I'm calling an electrician."

Mr. Machine blinked his red lights, green lights and yellow lights just for the hell of it. And he was humming some kind of love song, real loud. Then he blew a fuse.

90

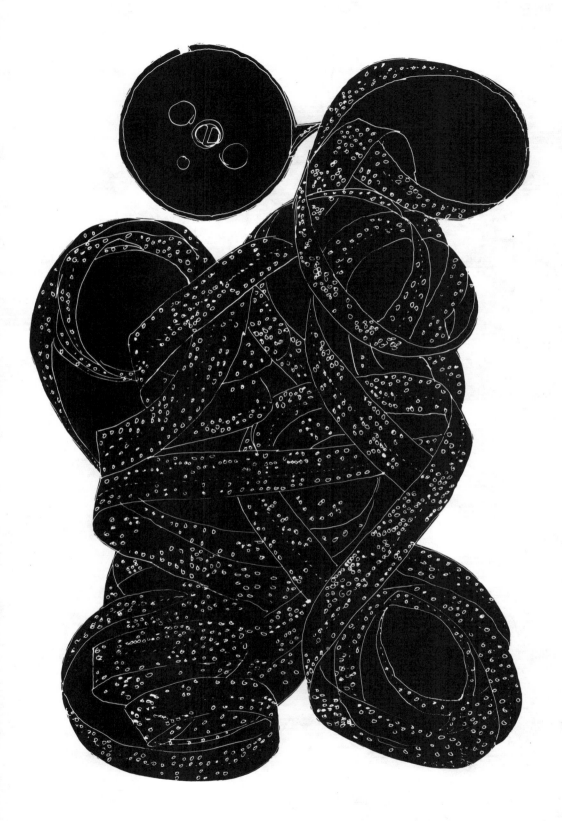

Day of the Magnolia Blossom

I WAS back in New Orleans, at the bend of the Mississippi near Thalia Street, looking for a banana boat to take me to Veracruz, where the beaches are wonderful and the water is warm and clear. As I turned a corner, I decided to drop in on Speedy Smith to let him know that I hadn't starved, as he predicted I would. I had worked for him some 15 years ago.

I remembered him as a man who knew what he wanted and didn't deviate an inch from his goal. Every minute of his life was devoted to becoming the richest printer in Louisiana, and maybe in the world. He lived in a bachelor apartment above the shop so that he wouldn't lose any time traveling to and from work. He worked from morning till night, six days a week. On Sundays he did his paper work, if there wasn't a rush job on one of the presses. He had his meals upstairs, hurriedly cooked to save time.

Very strict with himself, Speedy Smith was also strict with others. He fired men for talking on the job. For a minute of tardiness he'd dock an hour of pay. Three times tardy and a man was fired. He could get all the help he wanted because he paid well and his checks were good.

One morning the blonde secretary brought a magnolia blossom and put it on her desk. She was looking around for some kind of glass to put it in when Speedy Smith stalked into the office. With the back of his hand he brushed the flower to the floor and stepped on it.

"This is a print shop," he told her, "not a garden. Keep your mind on business."

Obediently she sat down at the typewriter, but the muscles of her neck were tightening. Suddenly she jumped to her feet, fists clenched, tears in her eyes.

"You're plain crazy!" she cried. "You'd better see a psychiatrist!"

She quit on the spot. And so did I.

And now, after all these years, I was back in New Orleans, looking for Speedy Smith's print shop. The place had become a warehouse, with gunny sacks of fragrant coffee stacked along the walls. I looked up Speedy Smith in the phone directory and was surprised that he had moved to the other end of town, away from the business district. He probably had built a big new plant, like he always said he would.

As I got off the bus I saw a man walking down the street, leading an old airedale on a chain.

"You're Speedy Smith?" I asked.

"My shop is right around the corner," he said. Then he recognized me. "You're the linotype operator. I could give you a job, but only part time." He paused before he added, "And I wouldn't be able to pay much. But if I had help, I could really grow."

"I'm not looking for a job," I said. "My banana boat sails Monday."

He seemed disappointed as he sat down on a bench, inviting me to sit beside him. He leaned over to help the dog settle down.

"Moppsie's old already," he explained. "She's got arthritis. She's also blind. That's why I have to lead her around on a chain. Or she'd be bumping her head into trees and posts."

Moppsie wiggled the stump of her tail as she looked up at us with her white blind eyes. She knew we were talking about her.

I offered Speedy Smith a drink from the flask of scotch I carried in my pocket. I knew he had a few things to say.

"Remember the magnolia blossom?" he began. "The girl told me I was crazy and I had the feeling that she might be right. So I went to see a head shrinker. He told me I was losing my capacity to feel like a human being. When I insisted that I was quite happy as a bachelor, he shook his head and told me to get emotionally involved with something that had a heart and soul. That's when Moppsie came into my life."

At the mention of her name, Moppsie wiggled her tail again.

"She was just a pup at that time," Speedy continued. "She ran into the shop through an open door and the first thing she did was to tip a can of graphite that some knucklehead had left on the floor. She skidded through the graphite and kept running back and forth, spreading the damn black stuff all over the shop. Then she began rolling around in it. I wanted to kick the damn dog through the door."

"Why didn't you?" I asked.

"A gorgeous redhead come into the shop, looking for a lost puppy. Normally, I would have told her to take the dog and get the hell out. But I remembered the words of the psychiatrist. He told me to be sympathetic towards living things. Well, this one was a living doll. How can you pick up a dog full of graphite and give it to a girl in a white dress? I yelled for an apprentice to wash the dog, but the kid was out to lunch. So I washed the dog myself, while the lady kept murmuring sweet nothings to the dog. I could feel the quick beating of the puppy's heart. Mine was pumping kind of hard, too.

"Then the lady remembered that she couldn't take a wet dog outside because it might catch a cold. She asked if I could take care of it until it dried. She told me her name was Gloria, and she didn't have a phone number because she was in the process of moving from one apartment to another. That's how the dog had escaped."

"And that's how you got stuck with the dog," I said, nodding as I opened the flask once more.

"That's just the beginning," said Speedy. "I took the dog upstairs and tied it to the kitchen sink so it wouldn't chew up the carpets or something. Then, remembering the psychiatrist's advice about human involvement, I put two bottles of champagne into the refrigerator. I figured Gloria might be thirsty when she came to pick up the dog. But Gloria phoned later that afternoon and asked if I could take care of Moppsie for a few days because the new landlord was crabby about dogs right now, but he'd simmer down. So there I was, living with a dog in my bachelor apartment. Instead of running the Miehle, I was walking Moppsie through the alleys. Instead of doing my estimating at night, I was wondering whether to give Moppsie chicken livers or hamburgers. She didn't like canned food. And she kept moaning until I let her sleep beside me on the bed, with her head on the pillow, staring into my face. I wasn't used to that kind of life. Give me another drink."

Speedy Smith paused before he continued. "After a week it turned out that Gloria's three children were crying to see their puppy. They wanted visitation privileges with the dog on

Sundays. I almost blew my stack. I didn't know she had three kids — all girls. But I remembered the words of the psychiatrist. I also remembered the two bottles of champagne.

"I had been thinking about buying a larger paper cutter, but I bought a station wagon instead. My convertible had become too small. We had fallen into the habit of taking the dog and the children for a ride on Sundays. I was ready to sign a contract for another offset press, but what did I do? I bought a house instead, so the kids could be with their dog and I could be with Gloria. Then she didn't want me to travel through all that traffic every day and pay all that rent downtown. So I moved the equipment into the garage in back of the house. I had to sell some of it, but I've still got one linotype. If you'd care to run it . . . we could get a lot more work . . ."

Speedy helped lift Moppsie to her feet and aimed her head up the street. We finished the scotch while walking.

The house was really big. Purple wisteria was climbing the trellises. Begonias and azaleas made the back yard look like a painting by a French impressionist. A clothes line was strung from the house to the garage. I studied the fluttering diapers.

"We have three more kids of our own," Speedy explained. "Two boys and a girl. But we've still got plenty of room. There's a cot in the attic if you'd like to stay. I can't pay much, but you'd get some mighty fine meals. Gloria's a wonderful cook."

I sniffed the air. "Shrimp creole?" I asked.

"We have it every Friday. And a big breakfast every morning. Now and then we have bouillabaisse."

Home cooking sounded real good to me and so I stayed. The beach at Lake Pontchartrain was only a few blocks away and I did plenty of swimming. And then, one evening, when all of us were working late, Speedy Smith asked me a question.

"Tell me," he said, "when was I really crazy? When I

stepped on the magnolia blossom? Or when I was washing the dog?"

I remained silent.

Gloria scowled as she looked up from the stitcher. "Go on," she insisted. "Answer him."

"My. banana boat leaves Monday," I said.

ABC aabc
DEF%def
GHI#ghh
JKL":" ijkl
MNO=¢nop
PQR@*qrst
RST!?uvw
UVW xyz

Generation Gap Comes to Printing Management

OLD Man Jackson did not believe in spoiling his only son. He insisted that the boy start at the bottom of the newspaper business and work his way up, in the great American tradition.

"Stonehead," the old man said, "your college degree is not enough. You've got to spend at least a month in every department so that you'd know what the newspaper business is all about."

"And then I become vice president?" Stonehead asked.

"Then you become vice president."

And so Stonehead Jackson had spent a month on the delivery trucks, a month in the pressroom, and now was in the composing room.

The first thing he did was to zero in on the machinists.

"Those guys are standing around, doing nothing," he complained to his father.

"Let them stand," the old man replied tolerantly, "as long as the machines are running."

"How do you know they're running all the time?"

"I trust my machinists. They're good men. They keep the machines going."

"You've got an old-fashioned attitude, Pop. I'll show you what I learned in college. First, we'll need a control room. I'll have it built in that corner. We can throw out a few type cabinets."

The old man shook his gray head. Then he remembered that a son begotten by himself couldn't be all bad.

"Go ahead," he said. "I'm glad you're showing an interest in the business."

One wall of the control room was devoted to a panel of 60 lights, one for each typesetting machine. When the machine was running the light showed green. When it stopped it showed red.

"See, Pop," Stonehead said when the project was finished. "You just look at the panel and you can tell which machine is running and which one is not."

"All I see is red lights. Forty-five of them. Why aren't the machines running?"

"They're being fixed."

"But why does it take so long? Last week I hired five extra machinists and I've still got 45 red lights on the panel. I've got to see what's going on."

The old man walked between the rows of typesetting machines. Operators and monitors were standing around, reading newspapers and lighting cigarets, while machinists were scribbling into large tabs of ruled forms.

"Hey, Curly!" the old man shouted at one of the machinists. "Why aren't you fixing this distributor stop? You've let the gate open."

"I've lost my ball point," said Curly.

"Here's a pencil."

"Thanks, sir, but a pencil won't help. The report has to be made out in quadrip . . . quadrip . . . four different sheets. And the top sheet has to be made out with a red ball point. I've got to find one so I can make out the report."

"What kind of report?"

"I have to explain why the distributor stopped. I have to specify the number of the channel entrance, the condition of the teeth and ears of the mat, the font number . . ."

"Hurry!" said the old man. "Get the red ball point." And he kept walking down the aisles between the idle machines.

One of the younger machinists, eager to make a good impression, came up to him.

"Sir," he asked, "how do you spell helical?"

"What the hell's helical?"

"A helical pinion gear, sir. I found how to spell pinion all by myself. I had to stand in line at the dictionary for 20 minutes. May I offer a suggestion, sir, for the benefit of the company?"

"Go ahead."

"Purchase a dozen or more dictionaries, sir. So the machinists don't have to stand in line."

"Why don't you use the parts catalogue?"

"We never get a chance to see it, sir. The foreman has it all the time. He's trying to memorize the big words."

The boss stopped at an open machine, studying the splash of metal on the floor. In the old days he had fixed many a back squirt himself, in less than five minutes.

"What's holding it up?" he asked, touching the molds. "The machine's cold already. You must have had it open for a half hour."

A machinist was fussing around with micrometers, thermometers, screw drivers, hammers, and the inevitable ball point pen.

"New system," said the machinist, wrinkling his forehead. "We have to give the reason for the back squirt. It may be due to high temperature or low temperature. The molds may be worn or the disc may be warped. The lockup may be off its feet. Or maybe the damn machine just feels like having a back squirt today. But I've got to fill out the form."

Through the corner of his eye, the old boss saw Stash sneaking away from a broken down linotype.

"What about this cracked cam, Stash?" he shouted. "You're an expert on replacing cams."

"Not any more, boss. I can fix the — — thing, but I can't spell it. I don't even know what to call it. I just call it a ring-arounder. I've been fixing ringarounders for 30 — — years, but I still don't know how to spell them."

"Goddamit, Stash, fix the — — ringarounder and the hell with the spelling."

"That's easy to say, boss. But last week a good machinist got fired because he made a mistake in spelling. And I'm on probation. Your son gave me just one more chance."

"Probation? What did you do?"

"In making out a report, I put the carbon paper in backward."

Old Man Jackson reached into his pocket for a couple of aspirins. And he took a pill for his high blood pressure. Indignantly he walked into his son's office.

Stonehead was sprawled in a contour chair in front of the red-lit panel. On his lap was a gorgeous brunette, revealing a lot of leg.

"Hello, Pop, Meet Suzie. She's my secretary."

"Secretary?"

"You didn't expect me to handle all that paper work myself,

102

did you, Pop? I watch the panel and she files the reports. Then we'll need a computer to tabulate the results so that we could draw a projection into the future maintenance problems. For instance, we'll be able to predict that on November 27th at 2:34 p.m. we'll need new brushes on the motor of Number 42. We'll also need an assistant who can run the computer."

The old man kept staring at Suzie, who fluttered her fingers at him.

"The first day on the job and you're on his lap already?" he asked.

Suzie stood up, brushed down her miniskirt, and extended her long-nailed fingers to Old Man Jackson.

"I'm happy to meet you, sir," she said graciously. "Your son and I are not exactly strangers. Stonehead was my roommate in college."

Threshold of Prosperity

S HE filled the doorway as she stood on the threshold. In her chubby hand she held a few sheets of paper.

"I'm Mrs. Bublinski," she said. "I bought the equipment of the Busy Bee Print Shop. We've got it in our basement. I was told that you'd set type for us."

"Gladly," I said, getting up from the machine. I had been trying to beat the 1932 depression by going into business for myself. With a Model 8 Linotype and two extra magazines I operated a typesetting company in a small wooden garage in Chicago.

Mrs. Bublinski showed me the copy for a church bulletin I had been setting for the Busy Bee until the very day the printer died. Now he probably was smiling, four days in the grave, confident that the bulletin was to be printed on schedule.

104

"How much will you charge?" Mrs. Bublinski asked.

"Two cents a line, plus metal."

"Two cents for every little line?" she asked incredulously.

Her blue eyes narrowed as she waited for me to cut the price by a half penny or so. I stared back at her until her eyes twinkled and we both laughed. She was almost old enough to be my mother, but she had an exuberant bounciness that made her quite attractive.

When Mrs. Bublinski picked up the type the next day she paid me in cash and gave me 20 pounds of metal. Then she said, "Please, Mr. Typesetter, will you show me what to do now?"

"Don't you know?" I asked.

"I know how to put the paper in the press and take it out. I used to watch the other printer, bless his soul. But I don't know how to put the type in the press. You'll have to show me. Just once. And then I won't bother you."

I didn't have any work in the shop anyway, so I walked with her to the basement, where an old Gordon press stood on a wooden platform. A husky young man was squatting beside it, glumly massaging it with a gasoline-soaked rag.

"This is Stashoo," said Mrs. Bublinski. "My son-in-law. I bought the business for him. He's been out of a job for almost a year. Just hanging around the house, doing nothing. So he may as well be a printer. And that's my daughter over there. Mary, say hello to Mr. Typesetter."

The pretty blonde, conscious of the smudge on her cheek, said hello. She was holding a composing stick in which she was setting a calling card for Stanley's Print Shop. She was using 14-point Gallia for the main line and was having trouble with the p's and q's in the smaller type, Cheltenham, it seemed.

Mrs. Bublinski excused herself for a minute because she had to go upstairs to put the soup on.

Stanley shook his head as I unwrapped the type I had brought.

"The old lady's crazy," he told me. "She's so damn nervous just because I'm out of a job. We've got no money and so we had to move in with her. She's got plenty of room upstairs anyway, now that her old man has hit the road. He couldn't stand her either. She just kept nagging him all the time because he lost a job. Hell, everybody's out of a job nowadays. That's no crime. But I ain't no printer. All I ever did was hit cows on the head at the stockyards."

Mary was wiping her hands in a towel. "Mother is only trying to help us, Stashoo. We've been living off her for almost a year."

I looked into Mary's innocent eyes, as blue as her mother's. "How about you?" I asked. "Do you happen to know anything about printing?"

Mary shrugged. "I used to sell candy at Woolworth's."

Conversation stopped as the wooden stairs creaked under the weight of Mrs. Bublinski. She hovered over me, demanding that everybody pay strict attention while I locked up the form of the church bulletin. She was thrilled when, two hours later, we finally got the press running.

"How beautiful!" she exclaimed, holding up one of the sheets.

Personally, I had never seen such a lousy job. I'm not good at makeready. From the basement I went directly to a movie to see Greta Garbo. I had enough of printing for one day.

Next morning, before I turned on the machine, Mrs. Bublinski was pounding at my door.

"I've got a rush job for you," she said, huffing and puffing. "Bingo tickets. I'll wait for the type. I promised them for tonight."

She was getting on my nerves, but there wasn't much of anything else to do and I needed the fifty cents. For fifty cents I could buy a loaf of bread, a quart of milk, four weenies, and a can of beans. So I made up the ticket and even put a fancy border around it.

A few hours later Mrs. Bublinski was back with the copy for the dance tickets for the church in the next parish. "And they want to put out a 16-page program," she said. "You'll show us how to put it together, won't you?"

She fell into the habit of dropping in to see me three or four times a day, always asking questions, always bringing in some kind of order. She was a very church-going woman, going from one church to another, all over town, picking up orders. Along the way she didn't neglect the butchers and bakers and undertakers.

One afternoon she plopped herself into a chair beside my machine. "I've just made a big deal," she said. "I bought out another print shop. The man was going broke, so he gave me the whole outfit for three hundred dollars. He wanted four. Now we've got two presses and a lot more type. And a better paper-cutter. My husband's making a new floor in the basement."

"Your husband? Is he back from Texas?"

"He wrote me for money, like he always does. And I told him to come and get it. That we've got plenty of work for him right at home. He's tired of running around, anyway. He ruined his stomach. He needs my cooking."

I had to buy a few more fonts of matrices to keep up with all the work that Mrs. Bublinski brought in. Thanks to her, I was turning the corner towards the prosperity that President Hoover kept promising.

Then one day she said to me, "We're moving into a bigger place. So we could put in a Kelly and print a high school paper. Would you want to move in with us?"

I wrapped the package slowly, gaining time to think. "No," I said finally. "I'd lose all my other accounts."

108

"But I'd get enough work to keep you busy," she said.

I didn't like the idea of having Mrs. Bublinski breathing down my neck all the time. Rush this job and hurry up with that one. But without her business I'd be back where I started, drowning among the deadbeats.

"Let's let things the way they are for the time being," I said.

"But we need a Linotype in our own shop," she insisted. "We'd get faster service. And save a lot of running back and forth. If you merge with us, you'll have a share of the business. If you don't, we'll have to buy our own Linotype."

I didn't want to merge with anybody. I wanted to feel free to go to the beach when the sun was hot and to the movie when the picture was good. I felt that I had been trapped too long in an old garage, and that being trapped in a corner of Mrs. Bublinski's shop might be even worse.

"Why don't you buy me out?" I told her. "I'll give you a good price. And you'll have all the equipment you need. Even a good saw."

She frowned for a moment. Then she said, "I've been watching you run that machine. It's not much different from a typewriter. I'm sure Mary would learn to run it. My daughter, you know, took typing in high school."

"I'm sure she'll learn."

"And if we have trouble you'll be around to help us, won't you? Just for a day or two, until we learn to run it."

I stayed with them about a week, showing Mary how to operate the keyboard and Stashoo how to change magazines and clean the plunger. I couldn't show the old man too much. He said he knew all about it because he once had a job running a punch press. Mrs. Bublinski paid me in full from the money she kept under the mattress and I said good-bye and took a train going west.

A few years later, when I happened to be back in Chicago, I

dropped in to see them. They had added two Miehle Verticals and another Linotype. They even had a second-hand Ludlow. They offered me a job and so I worked for them for a few weeks. I realized I could have become a rich man if I had merged with them. Then Mrs. Bublinski began to breathe down my neck again and I said I had to go to Key West. I wanted to see the new highway that had just been built across the Keys. Maybe I'd settle down and catch big turtles for a living. Or maybe I'd take a boat to Havana and write a book.

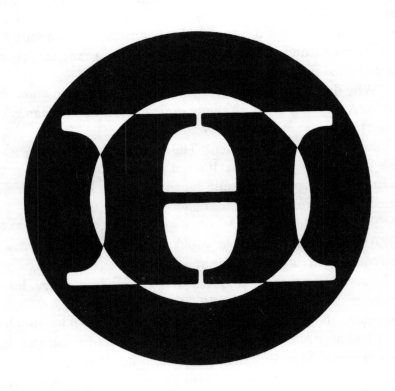

When Possession Was
All Points of the Law

THERE are times when every Linotype operator feels like a dismal larva trapped in a gray cocoon. He can hardly wait to break loose, spread his wings, and be a happy butterfly.

I was setting type in Nashville when I obeyed an impulse to become a rootin' tootin' go-getter of a salesman. I got a job with a dealer of printing equipment and exuberantly drove all over Kentucky, Tennessee, Arkansas, Alabama, and Mississippi. I peddled foundry type, slugs, and second-hand mats. I also took orders for machinery and collected bills along the way.

One day it was my duty to drop in at the Weekly Buzzard in the hills of Alabama. The proprietor was sitting at a Model C Intertype, working steadily. He was a gaunt man with furrowed cheeks and shaggy gray hair.

I swallowed hard to make sure my voice would have the proper authority. Then I said, "I've come to repossess this machine. You haven't been paying your notes."

The old man rose slowly to his feet, studied me as if I had crawled out of the woodwork, and reached to the wall for a double-barreled shotgun. He lay the gun across his lap as he sat down at the machine and continued setting type.

"You ain't gonna take no machine no how," he snarled.

"But, sir," I reminded him. "You haven't been paying. And I also have to take back that Ludlow."

The little old lady who had been standing at the Ludlow gave me a dirty look. She picked up a cushion, put it on the hot machine and, with great agility for her age, sat upon it. Staring at me scornfully, she spit into a spittoon and said, "You ain't gonna take my Ludlow neither."

"But, ma'am . . ." I protested.

The gun clicked as the man pulled back one of the triggers. "Don't you go giving no trouble to my wife," he said, "or I'll blow your head off." The other trigger clicked. I ran out, looking for the sheriff.

I found him across the street, leaning against the bank. Sun-bronzed, with cauliflower ears, he seemed to be expecting me.

"Look," I said, "I've got these repossession papers. The law says that I'm allowed to take the machines back. All I want to do is to get the machines on a loading platform so our truck can pick them up tomorrow. They're already sold to a newspaper in Arkansas."

The sheriff studied the papers, mumbled to himself, and accompanied me to the Weekly Buzzard.

"Look, here, Ebenezer," he said to the proprietor. "This man's got a right to take the machines. That's the law. It says so here in these papers."

Ebenezer kept setting type. His wife kept sitting on the Ludlow, mumbling horrible things about my ancestry.

Turning to me, the sheriff said, "You've got one hour, mister, to get the hell out of this shop with your machines."

"One hour?" I exclaimed. "I need a day."

"One hour. It says here in the papers that you should have a reasonable time. One hour is plenty reasonable. After that you can get shot for trespassing. And I mean that the machines have to be all the way out of the shop."

I decided to drag the machines through the back door out into the alley. I would throw a tarpaulin over them and stand guard overnight. Next day our truck would pick them up.

I ran to my station wagon, where I kept all kinds of tools. I didn't bother to lock my doors because I kept running back and forth. I loosened bolts, clipped electric wires, and tapped gas pipes. Then I ran to the local garage to get a tow truck with a winch. It took some time to find an additional ten yards of steel cable.

With eight minutes to spare we were dragging the Ludlow through the shop. The old lady was still sitting on it, trying to keep her balance as she yelled rebel profanities. The old man sat at the disconnected Intertype, fondling the shotgun as he watched the clock.

Then the sheriff barged in. "That tow truck's got to get out of there!" he yelled. "It's against the law to park in the alley."

The steel cable slackened. The garage mechanic unhitched it from the Ludlow and drove his truck away.

"And another thing," said the sheriff, rubbing his pancake ear. "Is that your car parked in front of the bank?"

"The station wagon? Yes."

"Right beside the No Parking sign?"

"There's no sign there."

"There sure is. C'mon look."

He was right. There was a portable No Parking sign right beside my car. I knew I had been framed, but I tried to keep my temper.

"Sorry," I said. "I'll pay the fine."

"There's more to it," drawled the sheriff. "It struck me kinda peculiar that a Yankee with a Tennessee license should park in front of an Alabama bank. You weren't aimin' to hold up the bank, were you?"

"Me? Hold up a bank?"

"I've got to examine your car," said the sheriff. "On grounds of suspicion."

"Go ahead," I said. "It's open."

"You've got some mighty fine bank robbin' tools here, mister. Crowbars, wrenches, wire clippers, dynamite . . ."

"Dynamite?"

"Eight sticks there, hiding under the tarpoleon. Eight sticks of dynamite."

"Somebody put them there."

"They'd come in might handy for blowing up a vault. We've got a nice little bank here, mister. We don't like no Yankees comin' down here to blow it up. And lookee here . . . a real nice tommy gun."

The sheriff pulled out a Thompson sub-machine gun, World War II vintage.

"That's not my gun," I insisted. "I haven't seen one of those for 20 years. Besides, it's harmless. The ammunition clip is gone."

The sheriff playfully fanned it along the sidewalk. "Rat-tat-tat," he chattered. "You could scare the hell out of our poor old bank president. I've got to lock you up, mister. You ain't up to no good."

He shoved me into the dungeon behind his office.

"This may take some time," he said. "I gotta check your

114

fingerprints with the FBI. Sometimes they work kinda slow."

"I have a legal right to make a phone call," I insisted.

He scratched his mangled ear. "Go ahead," he said, moving the phone so I could reach it through the bars. "The law says you can make a phone call."

Three times I tried to reach my boss in Nashville. Three times the local switchboard operator connected me with a cockroach exterminator in Knoxville.

The sheriff took the phone away from me. "The law says you're allowed one call. I gave you three. So shut up."

The following afternoon I asked the sheriff if our truck from Nashville had picked up the machines.

"Some kind of truck was here," the sheriff admitted. "But the driver couldn't find a place to park. This is town hall meeting day and all the farmers come in. On this day they're allowed to park everywhere, double park and triple park. It's the local law, you know. And there's so many cars around the Weekly Buzzard, even in the alley, that the truck couldn't get anywhere near the machines. So the driver did a lot of cussing and went back to Nashville."

"May I write a note to my boss?" I asked humbly.

"Sure. Here's a paper and envelope."

"Dear Boss . . ." I wrote.

Four days later the sheriff handed me a cheap postcard from Nashville. "Dear Otto," it said. "You're fired."

"Too bad about your job," said the sheriff, unlocking the iron door. "And you ain't even a successful bank robber. The FBI's got nothing to match your fingerprints."

"May I go now?"

"Go ahead. Here's the keys to your car. But I have to keep the dynamite and tommy gun."

"Keep them. They're yours anyway."

115

He showed big healthy teeth as he grinned.

"And another thing," he added. "I brought you a copy of the Weekly Buzzard. Right off the press. It's a pretty good paper for a town like this."

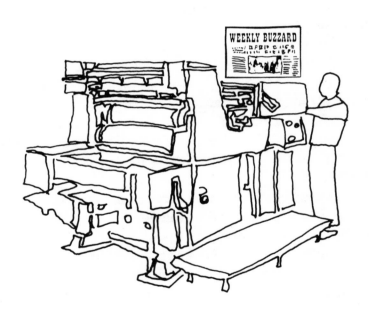

Living Is Doing
What You Believe In

HE sat alone at the bar, nursing a bottle of beer as he watched television. He had just finished his shift at the Daily Bugle and there was no place for him to go at two o'clock in the morning. There were the four walls of the rooming house and nothing else. There was no companionship there. All the other tenants had decent hours and were fast asleep already. The all-night tavern was a place where a person could unwind, relax, and talk to other printers.

But even in the tavern there was nobody who wanted to engage in conversation. Not with a man who was hitting seventy. The younger generation did not care to talk. They just sat and watched the tube.

The man seemed glad to see me sit beside him. Glancing at my hair, as gray as his own, he offered to buy me a beer.

"Work for the Bugle?" he asked.

"Since last week," I said.

"D'you like it?"

"It's o.k."

"D'you know," he said, "no matter how you wander around, you always remember the paper where you served your apprenticeship. Don't you?"

"I suppose so."

"It's like home. You remember the apple pie, but you don't remember the whippings. You feel a loyalty to your first paper, like to your mother." Tears glistened in the old man's eyes. "I ain't never felt so attached to any paper like I did to that first one. I was real proud of it."

"We all remember the first one," I agreed.

"But this one had tradition. Even General Grant couldn't put the Memphis Appeal out of business."

"D'you mean Grant of the Civil War?"

"The War of Northern Agression," the old man corrected . "When General Grant took Memphis he tried to stop the paper. It was a proud rebel paper. So he captured the print shop. But d'you know what?"

"What?"

"A week or so later he sees copies of the Memphis Appeal in the city streets. The same old rebel paper, telling everybody to rally around the Dixie flag. The paper was being sold right under General Grant's nose."

"How come?"

"The publishers were a pair of firesnorting rebels. Two colonels named McClanahan and Dill. They were newspapermen of the old breed, not the country club sissies you have nowadays. They saw that the Federal gunboats were winning the battle in Memphis harbor. So they loaded a press and some

118

cases of type into a box car and took off. They set up shop in Grenada, in Mississippi, about a hundred miles down south. They kept the same old masthead, though, the Memphis Appeal. They even kept correspondents behind Yankee lines. That was real journalism."

"A lost cause," I muttered, "They didn't have a chance."

"But they put up a fight," said the old man. "That's the main thing. They put up a fight."

The man looked much younger now that he was talking about something that interested him tremendously. It seemed that he had memorized the history of his first newspaper, the Memphis Commercial Appeal. And it was obvious that his memory was playing tricks on him. Although he had been born long after the Civil War had ended, his spirit was in that box car, with its press and type cases. He was escaping the dullness of modern life by imaginatively participating in the horrible but exhilarating adventures of the Civil War.

"The main thing," he continued, "is that they put up a fight. They didn't sit down to figure how much it would cost in dollars and pennies to keep putting out the paper. They decided that the paper would be published come hell or high water or General Grant."

"So what did they do when General Grant caught up to them?"

"He didn't. By the time Grant's army got to Grenada, the print shop was on a box car heading further south, to Jackson. For the next few months the Memphis Appeal was printed there. Same masthead. Same editorial policy. Telling Grant to go home. And calling him nasty names. Grant was sure mad at the paper. He'd send his cavalry ahead to look for the print shop."

"Did he find it in Jackson?"

"Just missed it. The print shop had moved east to Meridian. From there the box car went to Atlanta, Georgia. For almost a year the Memphis paper was being published in Atlanta. You've probably seen the movie 'Gone With the Wind.' Well, that's the way Atlanta was. The Memphis Appeal kept coming out while the city was burning. The Federal shells were bombing the hell out of them. General Sherman was taking the city on his march to the sea. The print shop was put on a box car again and moved to Montgomery, Alabama. Now and then, along the way, the paper was printed on a proof press. Those were real newspapermen."

"What did they use for paper?"

"Any paper they could find. A lot of times they used wall paper. And shoe black for ink. Sometimes they ran out of wood for the press. They had to keep feeding the fire to keep the steam up. It was a one-cylinder Hoe press. Wood was hard to get sometimes. Once when their fireman was looking for wood he came across a barrel of whiskey, just lying around. It was worth its weight in gold. Whiskey was selling for $2.50 a shot, the cheapest. The Federals were coming in fast, so the printers loaded the barrel into the box car along with the rest of the equipment. They must have had fun, putting out that paper."

"Did they do it for fun?" I asked. "Didn't they get paid?"

"Oh, they got paid all right. The typesetters were getting 75 cents a thousand ems and the pressman was getting $75 a week, Confederate money that is. But nobody got rich working for the paper. Eggs were $5 a dozen and coffee $18 a pound. No, none of the boys got rich. But they were proud of working for the paper. Proud rebels to the end."

"Didn't they get caught?"

"They had a lot of narrow escapes. From Montgomery they had to hurry back to Georgia. In Columbus a Federal cavalry unit finally caught up with them. Scattered the type in the streets, like they did to all rebel papers. They couldn't find the press, though. But the war was over already. Lee had

120

surrendered a few days before. Down South they didn't know about it yet."

"What became of the press?"

"It was hidden in Macon. Eventually it was put on a cotton wagon and hauled to Chattanooga. There it was put on a boat. Finally it got back, along the rivers, to Memphis. And the Appeal continued publishing in its home town. After three and a half years of wandering through the south."

The bartender brought two more bottles and we drank in silence. My companion blandly looked at the television for a while and then he said, "It must have felt important to be a printer on that paper. A man was really living, doing what he believed in. With cannons trying to knock his head off. Nowadays all we do is put in our time and pick up a paycheck. But we're not really alive. We're just numbers on a computerized payroll. If we drop dead, it's just a number missing. Tomorrow there'll be another number. There's no loyalty any more. How can you be loyal to a publisher you never see? How can the publisher be interested in a printer who is just a number? To him we're just a bunch of bums demanding more money. And all he wants is more money for himself. It's the only important thing nowadays. Just money. But there was a time . . ."

"Yes, there was a time . . ."

"There was a time when money was not so important. You worked for a newspaper out of loyalty. You felt that you were important to the paper. Like those printers putting out that rebel paper. It must have felt good to set the type that made General Grant cuss you up and down. It must have felt good to print on wall paper with bombs bursting in the streets. And General Sherman chasing you across Georgia. It made you

121

proud of being a printer. But this idea of working for nothing but a computerized paycheck . . . and spending it in a tavern . . . or on some fancy junk . . . it doesn't make sense. It ain't really living.''

Time to Be on the Go Again

FIFTY years ago a printer was considered well-traveled if he saw half the United States. Today the tramp printer thinks in terms of the world.

Douglas S., 42, has a home and family north of Vancouver while he works as a Linotype machinist in Chicago. "But I won't stay long," he insisted as he was fixing a squirt on my machine. "I have to keep moving. I want to work on the English paper in Hong Kong. I've got connections there. I've worked in Honolulu and Tahiti. There I set type in French. I learned to set French in Montreal, where I worked half the day in French and the other half in English.

"I've also set type in England. I do a lot of reading about small English towns and I wanted the experience of living in one. So I dropped in at union headquarters and told them I'd like a job in a quaint English town. A Dickensian character in a tweed jacket studied me over his spectacles and wrote a list of four jobs to choose from. I enjoyed working there very much. They have a relaxed attitude about everything. At High Wycombe we used to do our drinking at a pub called the Falcon and a few years later, back in Vancouver, I met the same fellow I used to drink with.

"Vancouver is a melting pot for printers. They come there from all over the world because Canada is liberal towards immigration. I knew a German operator who kept setting galley after galley of English with hardly any mistakes. But he couldn't speak English. He was just learning."

A few years ago Douglas took a grand tour of Europe. "My wife is Swedish and so we flew to Sweden to stay with her folks. We bought a Volkswagen for $400 and just kept riding around for almost a year, from Helsinki all the way down to Istanbul. European shops are becoming automated, but more gradually than in the United States. The people are not in frenzy about getting new gadgets. But they are very proud of their print shops. In Yugoslavia, for instance, a manager tried to impress me by showing me the composing room of his newspaper. I didn't have the heart to tell him that his equipment was obsolete and his paper was full of hairlines. Yugoslavians are very warm-hearted people. They're always shaking hands, patting you on the back, or touching you on your shoulder. They're not reserved like the English. The thing to eat on the Dalmatian coast is baby squids. We ordered them by mistake, thinking they were shrimps. They were absolutely out of this world."

Douglas said that he was offered a job with the Stars and Stripes in Darmstadt in West Germany. "But we were on our way back to Sweden, where we wanted to spend more time. Working conditions are not too bad in Europe. There is not so

126

much pressure. In most countries the law guarantees a four-week vacation. In Sweden people retire at 55 on a government pension. We sold the car for $450 and flew back to Vancouver. Now I'm working to save up money to buy a fishing boat. Boats cost plenty nowadays. But it's a good life, commercial fishing. I love the sea. It gives me the feeling of freedom. If I thought I had to spend the rest of my life fighting machines in a print shop, I'd go crazy."

Wayne C., still in his early thirties, has covered more territory than the average old-timer did in a lifetime. Instead of riding under box-cars, he flies. He and another printer have bought themselves a small plane. Flying is their hobby. They don't work their way from town to town. They hop 500 miles at a time. Nostalgically, he recalls working in New Zealand.

"It's a different world down there. People are very naive. They don't believe there can be such things as muggings and stabbings and getting hit over the head with a pipe. There's a child-like innocence about them. I'm going back some day."

And, because he enjoys surfboarding, he has fond memories of Australia. "Everybody hangs around the beaches down there. It's the real life."

The legendary tramp printer, however, is settling down. Automation has reared its ugly head and jobs are not as available as they were five or ten years ago. Right now the tramp gets a cold shoulder in New York City, San Francisco and Minneapolis. In Denver he may get two days a week. And the jobs are not good, anywhere. A linotyper may be required to hop around like a brainless dervish as he feeds tape into three or four machines. Helplessly he has to watch computerized hyphenization as "co-ok," "reknown-ed," and "ni-ght-club." If he is a hand compositor, proud of his skill with type, he may be condemned to scissors and pastepot, like a nut in a bughouse.

Among the deaf mutes who have given up wandering is James J. Irwin, now working in Chicago. Although totally deaf from scarlet fever since the age of two, he has spent many years on the road as a tramp printer. After learning the linotyping trade at the Milo Bennett School in Indiana, he worked in San Francisco, Texarkana, Des Moines, Little Rock, St. Louis, Dallas, Houston, El Paso, Denver and Baltimore. He also worked in small towns in Virginia and spent two years at the Government Printing Office in Washington, D.C.

With his lip-reading, sign language, and pencil and pad, he found no difficulty getting jobs wherever he went.

"My deafness doesn't bother me at all," he explained with his fingers and gestures. "Everybody has some kind of trouble and mine is not too bad. I am a most happy fellow."

128

But he admits he doesn't want to hit the road any more. "Too much automation."

A correspondent from Ohio says that tramping and marriage do not mix. About thirty years ago he left a wife somewhere in Kansas or Missouri and never got married again. That's really a shame — not knowing exactly where he left her.

My drinking buddy remembers specifically where he left his wives — one in Texas, another in Spokane, two in California, and the latest one in St. Petersburg, Florida. But he never gives up. Right now he is spending his week-ends on a farm in Indiana, helping a widow make some very potent apple cider.

The Hot Pants situation was handled discreetly in our composing room. Instead of competing with each other in displaying their charms, the Teletypesetter girls took turns. One girl wore her abbreviated pants on Mondays, another on Tuesdays and so on. Every night the limelight was on one specific girl, with no distractions.

Men began to pick their favorite nights. Consequently, many tramp printers stayed on their jobs all summer, despite their natural inclination to head for the north woods. When the girls went back to wearing baggy slacks the printers went south.

The Gold in Type Metal

I WAS having a pretty good time all by myself, running the Linotype while listening to Midnight Melodies coming over the radio, when Mr. Boss barged in. He was so mad he didn't even say hello. He just picked up a mallet and began planing down a newspaper form. He was banging so hard that I realized he must have had another argument with his wife. He hasn't the courage to fight her, so he runs to the shop to vent his anger on the delicate face of type.

Eventually he quieted down and began to fumble around in the type cases. Then we went to the Ludlow to set up a cover page for a musical program. Within an hour he was whistling quite contentedly.

Mr. Boss always rides out his emotional storms by working with his hands. As long as he has his print shop to run to, he'll never need a psychiatrist.

But Mr. Boss is a shrewd guy. Something in his mind keeps telling him that he has to make a buck on everything he does. So he goes to the petty cash box and takes out a ten-dollar bill as compensation for his hour of work. He leaves a note in the box saying, "Tips to errand boy — $10.00."

On this particular night he plugged in the coffeepot, filled two big porcelain cups and came to talk with me. On occasions like this, he's got to talk to somebody.

"We've gone so far off the gold standard it isn't even funny," he began. "We don't even use money any more. Everything is done with charge accounts and credit cards. My wife thinks her signature is as good as Fort Knox."

I kept my mouth shut. I don't want to get involved in family squabbles.

Mr. Boss sipped some coffee and put down the cup. "Our entire civilization is carried on with pieces of fluttering paper. Nobody sees gold any more."

"Too bad," I said. "I like to look at gold. It makes me very happy."

Frowning down at me, Mr. Boss shook his head.

"You're old-fashioned," he said. "Gold was all right in ancient times when people began using it as money. It was hard to make change in cows."

"Cows?"

"Cows were a popular form of money. In fact, our word *capital* comes from the Latin *capita*, meaning the heads of cattle."

"That wasn't so good," I said. "Bringing home a cow instead of a paycheck. I live on the third floor and my landlady is fussy."

"Don't worry. Those days are gone. Just like the days of gold are gone. We are now in the Great Paper Age, the era of confetti economics."

"I prefer gold," I insisted. "I'm sentimental about the stuff. The greatest love of my life was a widow with a big gold tooth. Down in Guatemala."

"Gold is a bauble for barbarians," said Mr. Boss. "It's not very useful. It's too soft for building bridges and too heavy for building ships. It's only good for making rings to dangle in ears and noses. And for seducing women."

"They're always on a gold standard, aren't they?"

"Always. With a nylon stocking a woman can dig more gold than any two men with a pickaxe. But what has gold really done for civilization?"

"It prevents inflation," I muttered.

"Wrong. A sudden influx of gold would cause inflation, like it did in Spain in the 1500's. And in Alaska during the Gold Rush. A nation's real wealth is determined by its production of goods, not by the amount of its gold. To a hungry man a beef steak is better than a nugget of gold."

I shook my head. "I don't agree with you, boss. Nobody gets *that* hungry any more. As far as I'm concerned, I like gold. I like the way it shines, like the sun, like the source of all life. There's something magical about it. All the people of the world have been dazzled by it. The Babylonians, the Incas, the Chinese. Everybody. Everywhere. King Midas loved it and so did Montezuma."

"Let's get out of the swamps of history," said Mr. Boss. "We're living in a modern age. We know that gold is not too rare. The oceans are full of it, a hundred fifty ounces per cubic mile. And every day the mountain streams are washing more gold into the sea. The Rocky Mountain chain must be loaded with gold all the way from South America to Alaska. So far we've scratched a few pinholes at Cripple Creek, Sutter's Mill and Klondike. But think of the areas we've missed. Some day

132

we'll learn how to find all the gold we want.''

"That would knock the hell out of the gold standard, wouldn't it, boss?"

"You're not kidding. The Rocky Mountain range actually extends into Siberia and keeps on going for thousands of miles. It's only a matter of time before Russia finds enough gold to upset world economics."

Having clinched his argument, Mr. Boss picked up a Margach bar of Linotype metal and hung it on my machine. Lovingly, he caressed the bar, which shimmered like silver. When he struck a match to light a cigarette, it reflected the golden flame.

"This type metal," he said reverently, "is more useful than all the gold in the world. It doesn't make trinkets. It makes civilizations."

I couldn't honestly share his enthusiasm. I didn't believe that I had given much of a push to civilization by setting 42 linear miles of Linotype slugs. All I did was to get from the Flapper Age to the Beatle Age, from flat-chested girls to mop-haired boys, from ballroom dances to epileptic dances. And maybe television is an improvement on vaudeville, but I'd rather see Lili St. Cyr in person, without having her bathtub act interrupted by a commercial for dog food. But why should I argue with the boss? That bar of type metal fascinated me.

"Perhaps you're right, boss," I said. "Perhaps that bar of type metal really keeps us rolling. And some day . . . some day . . . some bright boy will come around and convert the lead into gold."

Mr. Boss scowled at me as if I were a nut.

"You're back in the Middle Ages," he said. "That's the dream of medieval alchemists. But we know it can't be done. You can't change lead into gold."

"Don't be too sure," I said hesitantly. "The ancient chemists

133

didn't know much about atomic structure. They didn't have an atomic furnace, nor a cyclotron. They didn't know how to bombard the nucleus of an atom. Or knock an electron out of orbit. They didn't know how to speed up the disintegration of uranium into radium, how to change an atom of heavier metal into an atom of a lighter one. If the same process were applied to an atom of lead . . ."

"What are you talking about?"

"I said if you knocked a few electrons out of an atom of lead, that bar of type metal could become 18-carat gold."

Mr. Boss backed away from the machine and kept staring at the Margach bar. He kept shaking his head unbelievingly, as if it had turned to gold before his very eyes.

"All my type metal . . . all my type metal . . ." he kept mumbling. "My thousands and thousands of pounds of type metal . . . tons and tons of gold. Beautiful gold. Beautiful gold."

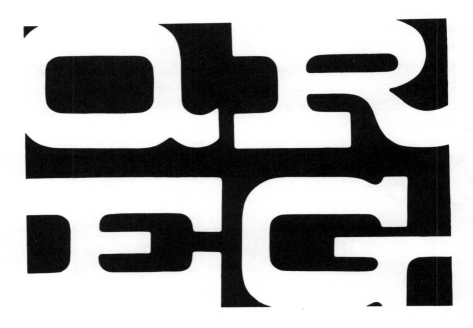

Apparition in the Night

I FELT very much alone that first night, sitting behind the Linotype of a small-town Michigan weekly. I was supposed to have quit at ten, but stayed till midnight, finishing all the news from local correspondents. I wanted to make a good impression on my new job.

Through the window I could barely see the blackened lake, so dark was the night. Neither the moon nor the stars sent down a glimmer to dispel the somber mood of the waves that lapped against the shore in a melancholy monotone. I closed the window to keep out the chilly air that felt like the cold breathing of a ghost.

I had foresworn to lay off the bottle, as much as possible, but the mournfulness of the lifeless lake had disentombed memories

135

of the past and with a trembling hand I reached for the fifth of brandy that I carried in my lunch box.

It would do no harm now, no matter how much I drank, because I was down to the last paragraph and the boss would be happy in the morning when he saw that I had finished all the copy on my very first night.

He had seemed to be a tough boss, rather old and crabby, and very strict about details. He had warned me about polishing my shoes.

I felt better after the drink. But as I looked out at the lake I saw that the rising vapors were forming huge cylindrical hulks that slowly kept advancing toward me across the sinister water.

Quickly I put out all the lights in the shop, hoping to find safety in darkness. For a long time, in petrified fascination, I kept watching the faintly luminous giants.

I had heard about the invaders from outer space who made landings in Michigan, but I had theories of my own.

The invasion would not come by land. It would come by water. The flying saucers would splash into lakes and oceans, where they could remain undetected until there were thousands of them. And the invading creatures, breathing through artificial gills, could advance along the bottom of our waterways, surprising us from the shores while we were scanning the skies.

Perhaps they wouldn't be visible to human eyes, being composed of some protoplasm that absorbed all light rays of the spectrum from infra red through ultra violet. The creatures probably spoke in high frequency sound waves beyond the range of the human ear.

They might be all around us, all the time, unseen, unheard, just waiting.

But as they rose from the relatively warm water, the chilly air of the night enshrouded each of them in a fog. They kept advancing toward the darkened shop, each platoon being reinforced by a new platoon rising from the water.

I took my bottle and kept retreating until my back was against the wall. There I stood horrified while one of those huge gray creatures came to the window, stopped to look in, then sank down towards the basement. And then another one came. And another.

I was afraid of the dark and afraid to put on the lights. And so I just stood there, taking a sip now and then to keep the shakes away.

Slowly I edged towards the door, determined to make a dash for it. But as my fingers touched the knob, I could feel it turning in my very hand. Jerking away from it, I could see, with eyes that were getting adjusted to the darkness, that the knob was turning again. But the door did not open. It was locked.

I sank to the floor helplessly, unable to even gasp for air. I might have passed out if it hadn't been for the brandy.

Then I heard the creaking of the basement door, the ominous groaning of rusty hinges.

A wave of cold, deathly air swept up the stairway from the cellar. I closed my eyes, shivering. For a long time there was silence . . . then the muffled clinking of tin cans.

More drunk than brave, I yanked a double-barreled shotgun off the wall, ran to the stairway and without even aiming, pulled both triggers. There were two clicks and nothing more. The gun wasn't loaded. It slipped out of my hands, clattering down the stairs. As I glanced down, I saw one of those white spineless creatures slithering up from the floor. I threw my brandy bottle at it.

I got to the newspaper early next morning to tell the publisher about his haunted print shop. Without speaking, he angrily handed me a check.

"I don't know what the hell you were up to last night," he said, stretching righteously to his full height, "but I can't keep a boozer."

The pressman was shaking his head. He was one of those handsome devils with black curly hair and long eyelashes. Without looking at me, he mumbled, "A boozer could do a lot of damage around here." I tried to remember where I had heard that mumbling voice. And I couldn't understand why such a nice fellow had turned against me.

We were standing at the top of the stairs, looking down into the basement.

"Beer cans all over the place," the boss complained.

"I don't drink beer," I said.

"And all that glass from a brandy bottle..."

"I saw something white. Like a ghost."

The boss looked at the clock. "You've still got time to catch the morning bus for Chicago. I'm afraid you just won't fit into a quiet town like this. We like it the way it is, nice and respectable. Nothing ever happens here, but that's the way we like it."

While the boss was speaking, his wife got up from the desk where she had been reading proof. She was quite a bit younger than he, but rather mousy, as if she didn't have the courage to act as pretty as she really could be.

"I'm going to the post office," she said quietly, "to pick up the mail."

She reached into the closet for a white raincoat which she draped over her arm. And she hurried out of the door, leaving behind her a barely perceptible trace of a strange perfume which I recognized as my favorite brandy.

Some Call It Freedom

NOWADAYS, with everybody so busy, busy, busy, it's almost a crime to be unemployed. Every man is rushing to a sunlit job in the morning and a moonlit job at night. But he isn't getting any richer because the world is in a conspiracy to separate him from his money.

Back in the depression, when a man had no clock to punch, he felt more free to hop a freight and see the world. He told his relatives he might find a job in Timbuctoo and they told him to go ahead.

Even in those days I was somewhat of a specialist, knowing really nothing except the positions of ninety Linotype keys. Away from the machine, I was helpless. Consequently, I developed a profound respect for the non-specialists of the open road. In hobo jungles, in the middle of nowhere, they managed to put together a pot of Mulligan stew.

Under a viaduct in central Illinois I met a square-jawed, red-headed young fellow named Alexander, who always carried a book in his hip pocket. He finished "Thus Spake Zarathustra" in Moline and, before crossing the Mississippi, he picked up a second-hand copy of Walt Whitman's "Leaves of Grass."

Alexander was reading the book as we sat on a bench in Fejervary Park Zoo in Davenport. I was watching a monkey on Monkey Island and the monkey was watching me, scratching his head as if he wondered whether evolution was going up or down. When he reached his decision, he tossed me a peanut.

"Lucky monkeys," I muttered out loud. "They've got a full belly and a place to sleep."

Alexander looked at me disdainfully.

"And iron bars around them. That's not for me."

Putting down his book, he told me that he had been on the go for six years already because he didn't want to be with his father, who considered him a failure.

"My old man named me Alexander because he wanted me to conquer the world. In other words, to help him build a printing empire in Ohio. I've tried my hand at every job in the print shop. But I can't stand the routine. I've got to keep moving."

"You've got to settle down eventually." I told him. "And learn to do one thing well. You can't be running away forever."

He glared at me scornfully. "Who the hell's running away? Not me. I'm walking forward to meet life face to face. It's guys like you who are running away from reality. In every town along the road you've been asking for the privilege of crawling into some stinking corner to operate a Linotype. You want to find some steady job so you could keep digging deeper and deeper into a rut. Till you can't see the daylight. You'll be trapped worse than those monkeys."

140

"Where do we go from here?" I asked, abruptly changing the subject.

"Do we need a destination?" said Alexander. "Can't we just keep going and see what happens? The world's full of surprises, no matter where we go."

When we stopped at a farm to do odd jobs for a meal, Alexander surprised me with his versatility. He could swing an axe, hitch a horse, change the spark plugs on a tractor and tell the difference between spinach and a weed. As a specialized Linotyper, I couldn't even milk a cow.

In the Sacramento Valley, where I found a steady Linotype job, Alexander put in a few days in an ad alley. For a while he was interested in the vineyards in the area and taught me how to make muscatel.

Then he took off towards the west, impatient to explore the lands beyond the Pacific. For a few months the post cards came quite frequently from places like Hong Kong, Saigon, Singapore... and then a card from Macassar... and much later another one from Wowoni... and then silence.

I thought of him now and then, when I'd be running a Linotype through the lonely hours of the night. I wondered if he was still walking the hungry road of freedom, or if he had settled down, at the end of the rainbow, feeding a press for three meals a day.

And then early in 1944, I saw this item in the Pacific edition of the Stars and Stripes:

"When the Marines landed on the tiny island of Sanana in the Molucca Sea they were amused to find that many of the native women wore sarongs imprinted with the words 'ALEX THE GREAT.'

"Old Chief Molumba explained that a few years before the war a red-headed young man named Alex had come to the island on a little boat. He brought with him many secrets of

141

civilization, especially pertaining to agriculture. He introduced new crops, such as sweet corn and watermelon, from seeds he carried in a small leather pouch. His skill as a carpenter was amazing to the natives. To keep him on the island, Old Chief Molumba gave him a luxurious hut and his most beautiful daughter. Alex became Prince of the Island, living the life that every man dreams of living.

"In his spare time Alex carved letters of the alphabet out of mahogany and made a crude printing press out of two slabs of wood. He printed on cloth with inks made of plants, minerals, squids, and octopi. One of the first things he printed was the

142

sign 'ALEX THE GREAT' in two-inch letters. The princess, unable to read, was so intrigued by the design of the letters that she insisted that he imprint her sarong. Soon all the women of the island wanted their sarongs to bear the words 'ALEX THE GREAT' in many different colors.

"Alex became a very busy man at his printing press, sometimes working late into the night. And then, one day, saying he was tired of it all, he got into his outrigger and said he was going fishing. He never came back."

The Lady Was a Printer

I T was midnight in Miami and The Lady was crying into her third martini. That's the trouble with martinis. You never know whether they'll bring fire or rain.

"I missed something in life." The Lady was saying, her eyes glistening in the intimate shadows of the cocktail lounge. She nodded toward a young couple romancing at the bar. "I missed moments like that. When I should have been having fun like other young people, I was running a Gordon in my father's shop."

"You're still young," I assured her. "Life begins at 39."

"Don't kid me," she answered, getting eye shadow on her Kleenex. "It's too late and I know it. I've thrown my life away for a shop full of equipment."

"You're one of the best printers in Chicago," I reminded her.

"Is that a compliment?" she asked. "For a woman?"

She gripped the thin stem of the glass and drained the

martini. "I came down to Florida to forget that I was a printer. I wanted to be what I never had time to be... a girl... a woman." She was sobbing again.

"We'd better be going," I said, realizing that the tomato was getting overripe. "We'll take a cab."

"No," she shook her head. "I want to walk barefoot in the surf in the moonlight. I never had time to do such things when I was a girl."

So I tied my shoes together and slung them over my shoulder. Carefully I rolled up the $17 slacks I had bought to impress The Lady. In her miniskirt she was running barelegged through the white foam of the sea. Like a dutiful beachcomber, I trotted after her, wishing I had worn my hobby jeans.

Finally she slumped down to a bench. I sat beside her, breathing hard — in fatigue, not in passion.

She laughed as she dug her toe into the cool sand. "I'm sober," she said. "Sober and happy. Martinis only make me cry. They make me want to be something I cannot be. But when I'm sober I like myself the way I am. A damn good printer."

As far as I was concerned the romantic evening was shot to hell. The woman was sober, my slacks were a mess, and I didn't know what to do about the sand on my feet.

"Maybe we need another drink," I suggested.

"No. My father never let me drink" she said. "He had no use for drunken printers. Same with smoking. He was always preaching physical fitness. He was a heavyweight champ in the Navy before he became a printer. Had a pug nose, cauliflower ears and everything. Wanted to have a son, but got me instead. And never had another kid, just me."

The Lady was looking into the distance as if she could see her father in a moon-silvered cloud above the sea.

"He was disappointed in me at first. He'd stay in his print shop late into the night, working and brooding. Once he got

146

picked up for smashing his fist into the sides of parked cars. That's how mad he was at the world. Then one day he asked me to give him a hand in the print shop. I enjoyed helping him. And he gave me a few dollars.

"I used to go to the shop straight from school, typing invoices and running presses. He showed me how to hold a composing stick. While other girls were picking out fancy dresses for the prom, I was wearing coveralls. While they were taking voice lessons and dramatics, I was listening to Pop holler Navy language across the shop. I learned to holler back at him. That's why my voice is so loud. I never had the time to cultivate a bedroom whisper."

"Didn't you marry?" I asked.

"Sure, I married. I married a compositor named Henry who worked for us. We had a busy season and so we spent a lot of time together in the print shop. Henry got along with the old man and so I married him. Pop was real happy. He said that now he had two sons working for him. He signed a lot of notes for new machinery because he had great confidence in both of us. We decided to postpone the baby until we paid off the two Heidelbergs. Then my father got hit by a car and died."

She sat silent a while, staring into nothingness.

"We missed him around the print shop," she said quietly. "We missed his booming voice, his gruff, rugged honesty. They don't make men like that any more. I couldn't do any work for a week. The place seemed empty without him and yet I could feel he was there all the time.

"I wanted to sell the place, get out of it, forget it. I wanted to become just a normal woman and raise a family. But we kept hanging on for another year, another. The business was really too good to throw overboard and Henry needed my help.

"We hired a girl to take care of the office. That made it easier for me. I had more time to devote to the house. I was even learning to cook. And then all of a sudden my husband ran away with the girl. Left a note saying she was a real woman, a real pregnant woman, and I was nothing but a chunk of printing equipment.

"And so I had nothing left but the print shop. I stayed in the shop from morning till night. The work kept me occupied. It kept me from going wild in my loneliness. And I kept hiring and firing until I got the right kind of help. And I made a success of the print shop, didn't I? Quite a success, didn't I, really?"

Her voice quavered, as if she were going to cry again. Then with sudden determination she shook her head and got up off the park bench. She carried her chin defiantly high as we walked to the lobby of her hotel.

Five or six women were lounging around, empty eyes staring through us.

The Lady Printer studied them as we waited for the elevator. "All my life," she said "I wanted to be just an average woman, with a husband, a home, and kids."

"Maybe... maybe there still is time," I assured her hesitantly, trying to keep the panic out of my voice. Suddenly I had become alarmed over the consequences of the Miami romance. I might be condemned to a lifetime of servitude at the Linotype, with a Lady Boss standing over me.

She laughed, as if reading my thoughts. Her voice was loud and clear again.

"No," she said, "it's too late for me to be just an average woman. I'm a tough old broad already. A damn good printer, but too independent to be pushed around by a husband. Or to be tied down by kids."

"Maybe you're missing something in life," I said unconvincingly.

"Sure, I miss the printing business. My vacation's over. I'm flying back tomorrow."

148

Profits in a Crystal Ball

I T'S pretty tough being a simple man nowadays. There's too much pressure. The psychologists keep pushing square pegs into square holes and round pegs into round holes. At the same time, the efficiency experts are eliminating the holes. By the time a man gets adjusted to his job, the job disappears.

When big business takes over, in baseball or in printing, the misfits have to go. There is no time to bother with pegs that are pentagonal, hexagonal, oval or just plain screwy.

There was a time when baseball had characters like Dizzy and Daffy Dean, Nick Altrock and Al Schacht. They used to have fun on the diamond. Zeke Bonura saluted line drives that whizzed out of reach. Rabbit Maranville, as a playing manager, used to bawl himself out for committing an error. Finally he fired himself. Joe Medwich and Paul Waner were human beings in uniform. They were not robots. Men like Tris Speaker and Ty Cobb did not wear numbers or names on their uniforms. Yet everybody recognized them.

Baseball used to be a game played by individuals. Today it is a commercial enterprise, conducted by an organization of business men. They frown upon the old-fashioned enthusiasm exhibited by the last of the do-or-die heroes, Jimmie Piersall.

And now that they have organized into unions we may expect a few new regulations regarding the speed with which a baseball may be pitched to a brother member. It may be declared unfair for a left fielder to catch a fly ball in center field, out of his jurisdiction. And nobody will suffer the humiliation of being tagged on second by a brother member.

Baseball players have been wearing gray flannel suits for quite a while. But now they're so involved in business matters that they may start carrying attache cases as they run the bases. There's always a chance of selling some insurance while stranded on third.

The coach on third will probably be a graduate on the Stanislavsky dramatic school.

"Smile as you slide," he will shout in a Russian accent. "You're on camera! And don't rip your pants. The ladies are watching."

Now that baseball has become a big business controlled by lawyers and accountants, baseball has also become a big bore.

Something similar has happened in the print shops. There was a Linotype operator who used to run around barefoot at the Chicago Tribune some 20 years ago. But social pressure became so great that this fine specimen from the Arkansas hills was forced to hide his individuality in tight-fitting shoes. When he hobbled to his machine, well shod but defeated, most of us felt sad. Something fine had been lost. A hero had surrendered.

An oddball eventually gravitates toward a small shop, where his idosyncrasies are overlooked. A small shop is like a happy family. It learns to live with its crazy relatives.

Once we had a Linotype operator named Max. He wore size fourteen shoes and a red pointed beard that extended 32 picas from the tip of his chin. He used to trim it himself, with scissors and a pica gauge.

After a few hours he'd get tired of sitting at the Linotype because his big knees kept getting stuck under the keyboard. Then he'd run the Ludlow.

He always worked nights so he'd have plenty of time for the track. He loved horses. With his elbows on the rail, he gazed upon horses with the benign expression of St. Francis of Assisi, who also loved animals.

Sometimes, when Max happened to be in a melancholy drinking mood, he would confess that he also used to love women, having misplaced a wife somewhere near Hialeah, another one near Santa Anita, and another one near Pimlico.

"Horses are better," he would say. "They don't demand alimony when they get tired of running."

Max knew how to pick horses. He kept a chart tabulating their past performances. It involved complicated mathematics. Every now and then he'd be bending over the Ludlow cabinet as if he were concentrating on some copy. But he would be working on his mathematical chart.

Mr. Boss would blow his stack.

"Get that machine going!" he'd holler. "And keep your damn beard out of the gears."

Max would smile tolerantly and say, for instance, "Put your money on Petunia in the fourth."

Max's hunch was usually good. We were all making money.

And then for some reason, while the horses were running at

Hawthorne, Max lost his magic touch.

Sympathetically I patted him on the shoulder.

"You can't solve a horse with algebra," I told him.

"Why not?"

"The beast has moods— just like a woman. There's no reason for moods. They just happen."

"There's a reason for everything," Max insisted. "But I haven't time to find the reason. I've got to get a winner for the boss. He lost ten bucks this week. He's got me sweeping floors."

It was then that we noticed a circular that was flapping off the Heidelberg. The headline was in 36-point Tempo Heavy Condensed. It said, "See Your Future in Madame Olivia's Crystal Ball."

Max pulled his beard reflectively. "I wonder if she can see a horse in that thing?"

Madame Olivia had a little store on Halsted Street. Green and yellow drapes gave the reception room a cozy atmosphere. She looked younger than I had expected. In her early twenties, she was long-legged and beautifully rounded. Her big brown eyes made me forget all about horses.

But she didn't even seem to see me. She kept looking up at Max. Showing her palms, she asked slowly, "Is that all you want? A winner in the third race tomorrow?"

"I play only one a day," said Max. "With all I've got."

"Take my hand," she said "and come with me behind the velvet curtain. That's where I keep my crystal ball."

Max came from behind the velvet curtain with a dreamy look in his eyes. Out on the street he mumbled, "Put your money on Annabel Lee in the third."

"She's 20-to-one. Why should she win?"

"Because Jupiter and Mars are in a straight line or something. It's all in the crystal ball."

Mr. Boss went with us to the track. We all put money on the

nose of Annabel Lee. Max bought five tickets at the ten dollar window, I bought three at the five. Mr. Boss, as usual, bought one ticket at the two dollar window.

Annabel Lee won by two lengths.

That night we celebrated at the shop, with Max buying the drinks. But he could not settle down to work. At midnight he took off, claiming a headache.

He didn't show up the next evening nor the next. Nobody

could find him. We feared that possibly he could have gone east or west or south, back to one of his ex-wives.

A month had passed and I was feeling in the dumps, just like a discouraged race horse that keeps running around in circles for nothing but a bundle of hay.

So I figured that maybe Madame Olivia might give me a psychological boost with her crystal ball.

As I opened the door, a bell tinkled. My heart pounded as I expected the luscious Madame Olivia to step through the black velvet curtain. Instead, I was confronted by a giant in a huge purple turban. He looked like something out of Aladdin's lamp. It was Max.

"Where's Madame Olivia?" I asked.

"She's out shopping," he said, smiling contentedly. "We merged, you know. She takes care of customers who have problems with love and I take care of customers who have problems with horses. And we're doing fine."

Printers' Christmas Party

MARA and Michael, the two children of Publisher Higgins, visited the composing room of the Daily Bugle every Christmas, to show that we were all members of one happy newspaper family.

Mara, with lustrous black hair falling smoothly over her shoulders, looked prettier than ever this year. There was a time when she had been a rich little snob, but the courses in modern art and existentialism had awakened in her a genuine sympathy for the working class. She kept in good shape by marching in every possible picket line. She even picketed her father's newspaper when the stereotypers were protesting against a leaky faucet in the washroom.

When she had bivouacked with the Yippies in the Battle of

Chicago she had a portrait of McCarthy painted above her right knee. Then she had to have her miniskirt shortened so people could see way up to McCarthy's intelligent eyebrows.

Michael, on the other hand, didn't have time for silly demonstrations. He was too busy trying to invent some kind of computer which would eliminate people.

In college he was working on a thesis entitled "The New Genesis," in which he was trying to prove that the creation of the world was the work of a Supreme Computer. On the first day the Computer created light. On the second day the 15-level tape divided the waters and permitted the firmament to appear. On the following days came the plants, the animals, and Adam and Eve.

On the seventh day, Michael's computer was programmed to make corrections, like deleting cockroaches. But it never got that far.

And so, with a tinseled tree on top of a make-up table, we waited for Mara and Michael to come to our Christmas party. We gave Mara two dozen long-stemmed roses, as we always did. And we gave Michael a half-gallon of very good scotch, being well aware of the refined tastes he had developed in college.

Michael didn't open his bottle. He merely kissed it and drank from our own bottles until Mara, with sisterly devotion, had to hold his shoulders to keep him from falling off a chair.

We sang "Jingle Bells" and drank a toast to Old Man Higgins, who had gone back to his home in the suburbs. Then we drank toasts to the Daily Bugle, to Mara, and to Michael.

Then Michael held a bottle high in the air and shouted, "To automation!" And he sucked the bottle dry.

"To automation!" repeated Pawlowski, a machinist. "Wait, Mr. Michael, I show you something."

And he pulled a tarpaulin off a huge tin box, almost as tall as a Linotype and just as wide.

156

"This is my great invention," said Pawlowski, with a dramatic flourish of his hand. "It sets type all by itself."

"A computer?" asked Michael, trying to focus his bleary eyes.

"Better than computer. I show you."

Pawlowski wheeled the big box to a Linotype and clamped it over the keyboard. As he snapped a switch a red beacon light began rotating on top of the box. Yellow and green lights flicked all over the sides. Pawlowski pushed a perforated tape into a slot and the keyboard began clicking. Hot slugs came down a

small conveyor belt.

Michael, slouched in his chair, kept watching.

"So what?" he said finally. "It's no better than the system we already have. And it's clumsier."

"Wait," said Pawlowski. "I show you more."

He pushed a sheet of typewritten copy through rubber rollers. Slugs came out, without errors.

Michael lurched to his feet and almost fell down. He leaned against the tin box. "D'you mean to tell me this gadget can read? It can scan?"

"Scan I don't know," said Pawlowski. "But read it can."

Michael's eyes bulged. "You've really got something there. Now we can eliminate the damn union men. And really make some money. Can I look inside?"

Pawlowski shook his head. "Too much electricity," he warned.

But Michael's hand was already on a latch. He was thrown back to the floor with a heavy jolt of electricity. In shocked anger he glared at the box.

"Very sorry," said Pawlowski, "I told you. Too much electricity. Must not touch."

Subdued, Michael whispered hoarsely. "That invention could be worth millions. We could rent it to publishers. At a hundred dollars a day."

"A hundred dollars a day?" Pawlowski's eyes opened wide. "I show you something."

He pressed a button and the beacon light turned from red to purple. Then he picked up a mouthpiece and said, "Merry Christmas to everybody."

The slug came out in 8-point Corona on a 9-point body. Michael reached for it, letting it burn his fingers as he deciphered it slowly. "Merry Christmas to everybody."

Then he jumped to his feet. "Five hundred dollars a day!

158

That's what it's worth! This is what we've been really aiming at. We've broken the bottle neck in communication. I've got to call my Pop. He has to see this."

And he staggered down the aisle towards the phone.

Mara, daintily nibbling at bon-bons, had been staring at the tin box with a smile of amusement.

"Where's Barrymore?" she asked.

Barrymore was a magnificently profiled linotype operator who did a lot of acting at amateur theatricals. He was always waiting for that magic call from Hollywood.

"He's acting somewhere," I told her. "You know, playing the part of Santa Claus. At some orphanage, maybe."

"But he's always been here at the Christmas party," she said. "This is the first one he's missed. I saw him in Chicago last summer. With the Yippies, you know. We rode in the same paddy wagon."

"He was on television," I said profoundly. "Getting his head cracked by the police."

"May I talk to that tin box?" she asked, reaching for the mouthpiece.

Pawlowski shook his head, but there was nothing he could do with a determined girl like Mara.

"Hello, you big gorgeous hunk of computer," she said. And the slugs came out, even with an exclamation point. Then she whispered something that we could not hear because Michael was yelling at all of us to come to the phone.

"But dad!" he was shouting. "You've got to come down here right away. This guy's really got something. It reads tape. It reads copy. It reads a voice. The damn thing's almost human. It's worth millions. No, I'm not drunk. I've got witnesses."

159

By the time we got back to the tin box the beacon light had gone out. The machine refused to set type no matter what we stuck into it. Pawlowski even shouted something nasty in Polish, but the machine stood obstinately silent.

And Mara had disappeared.

Come to think of it, Barrymore had really put on a good show in that tin box. He always claimed that he could set type better than any computer. Now he's bragging that he's going to do what no computer can ever do. He's going to reproduce himself, five or six times.

As the son-in-law of the publisher, he now has plenty of time.

123 456 7890?! AB EFGHIJ KLMNO FGH

ABCDEFGHI
JKLMNOPQ!
RSTUVWXY
Z&123456789

mnopqrstuvw
WXYZ

They Keep Selling
the Brooklyn Bridge!

IT was almost ten o'clock at night when Mr. Boss
came back into the shop, carrying a pint of vanilla ice
cream. He put some on my dish and the rest on his own. Then
he sat beside me at the Linotype, mournfully shaking his head
as he studied his mound of white stuff.

"Now it's come to this," he said defeatedly. "Doctor's orders.
Ice cream for my ulcer."

Then his eyes brightened up and he said, "But we just can't
eat it this way, can we?"

"I don't think so, boss," I replied, "I never eat it raw. Might
have germs. I always put rum over mine. Or maybe creme de

161

cacao, like I do on oatmeal."

Mr. Boss went to his desk and opened the fabulous drawer. "We'll try it with blackberry brandy," he said, making a quick decision, worthy of any great executive.

I knew he had trouble at home again, or he wouldn't be here in the middle of the night, seeking solace in ice cream.

"These women are crazy," he said finally. "A dozen of them are in the house, watching some kind of copper kettle demonstration. And I've been listening to them talk about how they throw their money around. For instance, one of them just got married two months ago. And do you know the first thing the newlyweds had to buy?"

"A bed."

"No. They sleep on a mattress on the floor like beatniks. But for six hundred dollars they bought a refrigerator that automatically makes a hundred ice cubes every three hours. They couldn't resist the sales pitch of a hundred ice cubes every three hours. I never heard of newlyweds needing so many ice cubes. Are they so full of vitamins, or something?"

Mr. Boss's voice had been rising indignantly, which was bad for his ulcer. I tried to pacify him by handing him a cookie out of my lunch box.

"Don't worry, boss," I said. "If they've got a lot of money, let them have the ice cubes."

"But they haven't the money. They're paying it off at $20 a month for three years. Can't they buy something cheaper for cash?"

"Those days are gone forever, boss," I told him. "Nowadays we enjoy as we pay."

"Does anybody enjoy paying every month?" he demanded. "Twenty per cent interest? Or take these new credit cards everybody is pushing down our necks. Any nitwit can run through a store, flashing a card as he buys anything from pretz-

162

els to motorboats, and poor daddy gets stuck with the small print which mentions 1½ per cent per month interest. That means he's going to pay $118 for $100 worth of merchandise that nobody really needs. I like to see people pay cash. They think twice before handing over real, honest-to-goodness money."

"Cash is out of style, boss."

"Tell that to the bankers," Mr. Boss replied. "Tell them to accept a credit card in payment of a mortgage. No matter how they approve of credit cards, when it comes to the final settlement, they never take anything less than cold cash. Deep in their hearts the bankers are no different from my grandmother. She used to run a Bohemian finance company under the mattress. If we needed to buy something, we borrowed cash from her."

"No interest charge?"

"We had to keep her supplied with peppermint schnapps. She always kept a bottle under her pillow, for sipping during the night. Kept her healthy till 97."

Mr. Boss smiled as he thought of the good old days. "You know," he continued, "we used to have some pretty good salesmen back in those days. Every few weeks the Brooklyn Bridge was sold to some farmer who gave all his money as a down payment."

"Things like that don't happen any more, boss."

"Are you kidding? What about that small printer on the south side who went broke paying for an $8000 paper cutter? He needed it like a hole in the head. The same guy who had sold it to him for eight grand bought it back at the auction sale for eleven hundred dollars. I think it was lousy salesmanship in signing up that little printer for such an expensive paper cutter. It was like selling him the Brooklyn Bridge."

I shook my head. "That's not the salesman's problem, boss.

The guy should know what he's buying."

"In a civilized society it should be a salesman's problem. He should know what a man needs and what he can pay for. Take that new printer that opened up down the street. I think the salesmen are keeping him doped up on LSD. For $100 down and $50 a month he bought a small duplicator. He plans to get 5000 impressions an hour, at $3 per thousand. He is willing to work ten hours a day, six days a week. That's $900 a week profit, as he calls it."

"That's good money, boss."

"Well, last week when he got a bill from a typesetter, he flipped. Immediately he made a down payment on a cold-type outfit which will cost him $60 a month for three years. He figures he'll get all the composition free because his wife will set the type at home in her spare time. She'll do the paste-ups between the changing of diapers. They've got two small kids, you know."

"Poor kids."

"That's not all of it," continued Mr. Boss. "In renting the store he signed a two-year lease at $100 a month. So now he's over the barrel. ' lot of money going out and very little coming in. He's not a professional printer and the quality of his work is poor. He's lucky if he gets 2000 impressions a day, and he keeps cutting prices to get any kind of work at all."

I shrugged. "Serves him right, boss. He should figure things out for himself."

Mr. Boss shook his head. "But why should his family suffer? And why should the printing industry suffer? A starving printer gives a bad name to the entire profession. Why didn't the salesmen tap him on the shoulder and tell him to stay out of the printing business? Why didn't they tell him that no printer makes $900 a week running a small duplicator? Why didn't somebody tell him that he didn't have sufficient volume to

164

maintain his own typesetting plant? Why did everybody gang up on this dreamer, ruining him and his family, by selling him a Brooklyn Bridge?''

The Human Side of the Job

DURING the depression it was easy for a Linotype operator to take a few days off. All he had to do was ask a sub to take his place. There were always plenty of subs hanging around, hoping to get a day's work. In 1930 the slipboard of the Chicago Tribune carried the names of more than 70 unemployed subs. On an average afternoon there were 30 of us waiting in the hallway. Five or six got hired for the day. A sub at the bottom of the list was lucky if he got a day's work every three weeks.

Conditions have changed. New machines have replaced the old. I was working for a small shop in 1937 when the boss installed a new Intertype with a marvelous attachment, a quadder. Printers from all over used to come to watch me run it,

167

centering lines automatically. They predicted that a great many men would be thrown out of work. Now school kids come to watch me feed tape to a machine in Iowa. They nod their heads as their teachers solemnly predict that men like me will soon be out of work. Yes, everything has changed — except me. I'm still a bum.

"Hey, boss!" I yelled the other day. "I wanna take off for a few days. To visit New York."

"You'll have to find a sub," he said.

"Where?"

"There are none."

Well, it looked as if I'd have to quit again, after having accumulated three months of seniority, which is quite a bit for me. I never believed in seniority anyway. It paralyzes the body and mind, isolating a person from new places and new ideas.

Just then I heard two executives bellowing at each other.

"That's the whole damn trouble!" one of them was yelling. "We're paying the men too much money to run these machines. We don't need craftsmen anymore. The work has become so simple that any baboon can run a typesetting machine."

The next morning I went to the zoo to visit Babby the Baboon, an old friend of mine. With a harem of lady friends, he lives in a cage bigger than my apartment.

He's always eager to communicate, not with English words, but with grunts, snorts, smiles and scowls, eloquent gestures, and with the blinking of his eyes. He is much more communicative than the average human being. He doesn't keep his nose stuck in a newspaper. He doesn't spend his time staring, like a mute zombie, at a television tube.

"Babby," I told him. "I'm a Linotype operator at the Daily Mixup. I want you to be my substitute. I know you can do the job because the production manager said so."

Babby jumped up and down, eager to do me a favor.

168

"When do I start?" he squealed.

"Next week. All you have to do is to feed tape into a machine. Like this." I showed him a piece of tape I had brought.

"Can do. Nothing to it. Bring the machine."

"You've got to go over there."

"I hate the traffic. Air pollution. But I'll go. So I'll run the tape through the machine and then what?"

"Then you put another tape in. And another and another. All day you keep running tape through the machine."

"All day?" Babby's eyes popped wide open. "I'll try anything for five minutes. But I won't do it all day. Life is too precious. I'd miss the sunshine."

"You can work nights."

"Sleep is precious. Besides the job sounds too boring for a baboon."

"The tape comes in pretty colors," I said coaxingly. "Yellow and pink. Maybe they'll make it in red, green, and lavender to make the job more stimulating. As soon as the industrial psychologists get into the business."

"Still sounds dull," said Babby. "Why should a self-respecting baboon spend all his time pushing tape? There are so many other things to do." He glanced over his shoulder at his companions who were eavesdropping from behind a log.

"You'd be paid," I continued. "Two hundred bananas a week."

He blinked. "That's a lot of bananas. More than I can eat. What would I do with them?"

"You'd save them. And you'd buy yourself a plantation full of banana trees. And no baboon would be permitted to live on the plantation unless he paid you rent, in bananas. And no baboon would be permitted to pick a banana because they'd all be yours."

"The baboons would starve."

"No, they wouldn't. You'd magnanimously give them a job. You'd hire them to gather bananas from your trees. For every dozen bunches they picked, you'd give them four solitary bananas. Then you'd take two back for taxes and interest. Think of all the bananas you'd have."

Babby scratched his head. "I'd never be able to keep track of all those bananas."

"You'd hire a smart baboon to do the counting. For every thousand bananas he counted, you'd give him one."

"What if he took two?"

"He'd be an embezzler. You'd have him locked up."

Babby strutted about the cage, deep in thought. Then he said, "Funny thing about you human beings. You're always having things locked up. Every Fourth of July your politicians come to the park to make speeches about freedom. But you really believe in cages. You put everything into cages. Birds. Fishes. Elephants and gophers. Butterflies and crocodiles. Young people and old people. I don't blame you for putting chimpanzees in cages. They belong there. They're crazy."

"Chimpanzees crazy? Why do you say that?"

"They're always imitating human beings. Riding around on bicycles for Ed Sullivan. You never saw a self-respecting baboon do that. Or choke on a cigar. I know what's going on, you know. They even bring those televisions to the zoo nowadays!"

"What about the job?" I asked, getting back to the subject. "Are you going to be my substitute?"

"No. I don't need so many bananas. Besides, I think something's wrong with your system. To me it looks like a pile of bananas in one corner of the cage and a gang of hungry baboons in the other corner. I'd hate to be the one to keep them apart."

"With that attitude you'll never get anywhere," I said.

170

He showed his teeth in a huge grin. "How about yourself?" he asked. "How far did you get?" Casually he peeled a banana that had been purchased with my tax money.

Avoiding the question, I said. "Then I'll have to ask Chippy the Chimpanzee."

The baboon nodded. "Chippy's the perfect specimen for the job. He's always skidding down the road of evolution, trying to be human. The other day he was playing with a stick of dynamite, like you people play with atom bombs."

"He'll get two hundred bananas . . ."

"No bananas," said Babby. "You don't have to give him bananas. Just give him a cigar and a pat on the back. Chippy will do anything for prestige. He'll run up and down the aisles with coils of tape around his neck. He'll leap from one machine to the other to keep them all going. He'll even ride on roller skates to cover more territory. Just pat him on the back and give him a cigar."

I stood silent, closed my eyes and tried to visualize what the baboon was telling me.

"Well, aren't you going to ask him?" Babby insisted. "His cage is right down the road."

"No," I said softly, shaking my head.

"Why not?"

"I might get jealous."

"Jealous? Of what?"

"They'd make him a foreman."

Reading Is Believing, Too

CASEY was glad that he had finally found a home. It was only a single room, but it was his. He had a bed with linens and a little refrigerator with a steak in it. He had some cans of soup on a shelf and a pot of coffee on a small gas stove. He had a home. He even had a second-hand television set.

At the age of 55 Casey knew how to appreciate these things, even if his room was in back of a print shop in the middle of South Dakota, in the middle of nowhere.

He had blundered into the shop a few months ago, when he got stranded in this town, hungry, with no place to sleep. And he saw the printer working late at his type cases.

"I'm not much of a printer any more," Casey said, "but I could be of some help to you."

"I could use help," Mr. Boss said. "Any kind of help." He was

172

getting gray around the ears and his shoulders sagged as he kept putting type into a composing stick.

Casey enjoyed working in the shop. The equipment was old, all letterpress. It was the same kind of equipment he had learned to run as an apprentice many years ago. And the Linotype was a simple Model Five. He still knew how to clean the plunger and the magazine. He could set type on it, slowly but carefully.

Mr. Boss seemed glad he had somebody to talk to. "I had high hopes when I was young," he said one day. "I thought the town would grow, but it didn't. I used to have a weekly newspaper, but now the town's got a shopper. It's printed in the big city. While my wife was living she was a big help, but now . . ."

"We'll get things going again," said Casey. "You need help, that's all. I'll do my best."

And Casey really tried hard. He was willing to remain stuck in South Dakota for the rest of his life. He had been a hobo too long. It felt good to be "eatin' regular."

Mr. Boss seemed happy. He would smile at customers instead of being crabby with them. He would put an artistic touch to his typography instead of hurriedly slapping the type together. On Sundays, instead of doing paper work, Mr. Boss would go fishing with Casey. They never caught much, but it felt good to sit under the willows and talk.

"Never had a chance to do much of this," Mr. Boss would say, "I've always been too busy. Didn't even have a chance to travel. Only once. To the Bad Lands. A hundred miles away. Ever been there?"

Casey nodded. "I've been everywhere."

"According to legend, the ghosts of Indians live there. In the caves."

"Hard to find water."

"But the beauty of the stark, barren cliffs . . ." Mr. Boss was talking like one of those books in his library. "Mother Nature is really wonderful."

"Mother Nature is a bitch."

Mr. Boss angrily clenched his fishpole and went farther up-stream, to be alone. Casey realized he had offended the man. He'd have to watch himself or lose a happy home.

So when Mr. Boss would talk about the wonderful things he had read in books, Casey would nod in agreement. To the boss the High Sierras were magnificent. To Casey they were the place where Mother Nature, screaming her head off, had tried to kill him in a blizzard. Mr. Boss would speak on the unending grandeur of the Pacific Ocean. Casey silently remembered the undertow that had swept him out to sea. By conserving his strength and riding the waves he managed to make it back. And what did Mother Nature do? She slammed him against a reef, ripping his shoulder. The big scar was still there, as though from a machete.

"And the desert itself is not really dead," Mr. Boss would say, showing beautiful pictures of the Mojave. "The generosity of Mother Nature is apparent everywhere."

"It sure is," said Casey, remembering the time he was baking in the desert, his lips blistering. He couldn't even find a decent clump of cactus, so he could suck moisture from its pulp. And what did Mother Nature do? She sent him a rattlesnake for company. "Yes, Mother Nature sure is wonderful."

"You'd enjoy reading Thoreau," said Mr. Boss. "He spent a year by a lake, just studying nature and reading Greek."

"Never heard of him."

"Walt Whitman wrote about the people of America, the farmers, the carpenters . . ."

"Down in Arizona, ten years ago . . ." Casey paused. He didn't want to talk about the goons who chased the hoboes off the freight cars. With clubs and baseball bats. And when they beat the hell out of them they charged them with vagrancy and

174

sent them to the work farm.

Mr. Boss was still dreamy-eyed. "There is a camaraderie among the gentlemen of the road . . ."

Casey remembered the click of a switchblade in the pitch-black freight car. He stayed awake all night that time, his own knife in hand, ready to fight for his life.

"California is the best, isn't it?" asked Mr. Boss one evening.

"California is the very best," Casey agreed honestly. "California has been settled by wanderers and it still has respect for them. The Southern Pacific railroad is the best in the land. Their men even tell you where the freight trains stop, so you can make your plans. They don't kick you off into ditches, at high speed, like they do on other railroads. There used to be a wonderful hobo jungle at Santa Barbara, but they changed it into a zoo. But you can always get a meal and a bed at the Salvation Army. They'll give you clothes and shoes, if you need them. Or you can stay at the mission. Check in before six o'clock and you'll get a good supper. But they won't let you get out until five in the morning. And they won't let you smoke. I got the nicotine fits there one night and ran out into a storm. I wanted to smoke so bad. I slept under a bridge, but I didn't do much smoking. My tobacco got wet."

Casey and the boss would stay in the shop almost every night, working and talking. It was getting to be a good life for each of them, a comfortable living without much pressure. And when they'd close the shop Mr. Boss would go upstairs to his apartment to read more books and Casey would go to his room to watch television. He would smile contentedly as he lit his pipe. This good life might last a long time if he kept humoring the boss, telling him a new story every day, a pleasant story, the kind the boss liked to hear.

One afternoon as Casey was two-fingering the Linotype, Mr. Boss tapped him on the shoulder.

175

"Shut off the motor," he said. "We're going to celebrate."

"Celebrate what?"

"My resurrection. The opening of my eyes. You showed me how to live."

"Me?"

"You made me realize that I've been dead here in the middle of South Dakota. I've been letting the sands of time sink from under me and soon I'd disappear without a ripple."

"You've been drinking, boss. I can tell from the way you're talking."

"I've just sold all the equipment to a dealer. Even the building. Come on. Let's celebrate."

Casey felt a chill come over him. The white linen . . . the steak . . . the refrigerator . . . the gas stove . . . the television . . .

"And what are you going to do?" Casey asked nervously.

"I'll hit the road and be a bum."

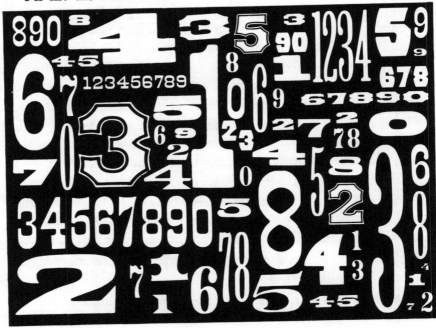

Comrade Jozef's $1000 Nose

DURING the depression of the thirties we had no war to worry about, no draft, and no atom bomb. We were interested in communism as a form of social philosophy, but we did not regard it as a menace. We were convinced that mass starvation in Russia would put an end to Lenin's dream.

In America the Communist Party was represented on the ballot during elections. William Z. Foster ran for President of the United States on the Communist ticket in 1924, 1928, and 1932. Earl Browder ran in 1936 and 1940.

Communist newspapers were published in many languages. The Daily Worker was displayed on the stands beside the New York Times. When my job folded under me I found myself linotyping a few days a week for the Chicago Daily Record, a communist tabloid which soon ran out of money. Then I bounced around from one shop to another, getting a political education while setting type in Czech, Slovak, Slovene, Croatian, Polish, Spanish, and a bit of German, where I had trouble because I couldn't read the Gothic script handwriting. Besides working for capitalists and communists, I also set type for anarchists and socialists.

Finally I got connected with a typesetting outfit that specialized in foreign language publications. One of our tabloid dailies was supported by the Communists. We'll call it the Balkan Red Star.

One evening it was my job to collect money from its publisher. His office was in back of the Communist Grocery Store, a block away from the print shop.

Comrade Josef glared at me from behind his desk. "I haven't the money," he said, lowering his shaggy gray eyebrows. "At midnight you call me down here. What good does it do? I just haven't the money."

He slapped the desk with a huge pudgy hand. He looked like a peasant who belonged behind a plow. He was proud of looking like a peasant. Communists trusted a man who looked like a peasant. Even when he carried the red flag in May Day parades, Comrade Jozef let his shirt hang out, like a peasant.

Besides being publisher of the Balkan Red Star, he was also treasurer of the Communist Grocery Store. He knew the combination of the big safe in the corner.

"The forms are locked up," I said, glancing at the clock. "But we won't send them to the pressroom until I get the money. Ninety-six dollars. Cash."

"My credit . . ."

"You owe five hundred already. From now on it's cash on the line. Every day."

178

He tossed his wallet to me. "There's forty dollars in there. Take it."

"Not enough. How about the money in the safe?"

Comrade Jozef raised his hands in protest. "That money belongs to the grocery."

"What's more important?" I asked. "The newspaper or the grocery? There are a lot of grocery stores, but only one Balkan Red Star."

"The paper is more important," he admitted, nodding his head. "Without it we are lost. The newspaper keeps us together."

With his elbows on the desk he buried his moon face in the palms of his hands. "I wouldn't have to be begging like this," he mumbled, "if I'd only get cooperation. Especially from my relatives. They all want to be on the payroll but none of them wants to work. Take my son-in-law, for instance. That book he's writing. Two columns every day we print of it. What do you think of it?"

I shrugged silently.

"He quit his job as a barber and decided to become an editor. So I put him on the payroll. Now he wants to be a Dostoyevski. All the time he's working on his book. He thinks he'll go to Hollywood and become a millionaire and the hell with the proletariat."

"The forms are waiting," I repeated, still staring at the huge safe. "All I want is ninety-six dollars."

Comrade Jozef looked at the safe, but shook his head. "Last week I sold a full page ad to the Big Shoe Company. It featured shoes for working people. I almost got a contract for one hundred dollars a week of advertising. And what did my son do? Not my son-in-law. My own son. My own flesh and blood. It was really my fault for sending him to the university, where he got such crazy ideas. He wrote an editorial telling people not to

179

patronize the Big Shoe Company. He said it was taking bread away from the mouths of poor shoemakers. And that was the end of the contract. And you think it's easy running a newspaper."

"Why don't you get the little shoemakers to advertise?"

"They aren't communists. They consider themselves business men. They're middle class. They want to be capitalists."

"The grocery store must be making money," I said. "Maybe you can borrow from the safe."

"The grocery store making money?" Comrade Jozef snorted. "With my brother-in-law running it? He put on 30 pounds since we made him manager. All the time we're running short of limburger cheese and salami. When a customer comes in, he says, 'Go away. Can't you see I'm eating?' Now he wants a liquor license so he could sell beer. Imagine him with limburger and rye bread and an ice box full of beer. He'd lock himself in the store so nobody would bother him. And his belly would bust."

"But there must be some money in the safe," I insisted.

"There is. The committee put it there. A thousand dollars they raised to keep the grocery going. But all the women shop in the chain store. My own wife. I asked her how come she didn't buy a bar of soap in our own store. She told me it was a penny cheaper in the capitalist store. She walks two blocks right past our own store to save a penny on a bar of soap. My own wife."

"The pressmen are waiting."

"The grocery store I can do without," said Comrade Josef, slowly rising from the chair and walking towards the safe. "But the newspaper I need . . . for political reasons . . . maybe some day I will be a senator. . . . Will you please punch me in the nose?"

"What did you say?"

"Will you punch me in the nose?" His eyes were serious. "I can't just hand the money over to you. The committee would fire me. But if you'd beat me up and made me open the safe . . ."

He took out a thousand dollars in four rolls of tens, with rubber bands around them. "This ought to keep the paper going a while," he said. "Now if you will punch me in the nose . . ."

I put the money in my pocket and clenched my fist. His eyes were closed shut, as if he expected excruciating pain. But I couldn't hit him.

"What's the matter?" he asked, cautiously opening one eye.

"I don't know. I just can't do it. I'm going back to the shop to get the presses rolling."

"But I've got to make it look like a hold-up."

He was still standing at the open door when I turned the corner. In the print shop there was a feeling of relief when I sent the forms to the pressroom. Jozef's son-in-law, the novelist, was especially happy.

"I've got to get back to the typewriter," he said. "To write tomorrow's installment. I left the heroine in the office of a Wall Street capitalist. He's undressing her."

But before the novelist could settle down to the seduction scene he was called to the phone. Protesting that he could not abandon the heroine at such a delicate moment, he nevertheless walked out into the street. A few minutes later he was back at the typewriter, nursing a bruised knuckle. He was laughing as he typed.

We stopped the presses to insert a bulletin on the front page.

"Comrade Jozef, publisher of the Balkan Red Star, was beaten last night by two hold-up men. They forced him to open the safe of the Communist Grocery Store. They escaped with one thousand dollars. Comrade Jozef suffered a broken nose."

181

Christmas in Dubuque

ALBERT was one of those men who don't make much of a ripple in passing through life. He was born in Dubuque, graduated from high school in Dubuque, served his apprenticeship in Dubuque, and got a job with the Dubuque Telegraph-Herald. A long time ago, when I spent some time in Dubuque, I got to know him real well. We ran Linotypes side by side.

"Don't you want anything better than this?" I asked him. "Don't you want to see the world?"

He scratched his head. "No," he said, his eyes twinkling. "I've got everything I want right here in Dubuque."

Personally, I've never had anything against Dubuque. I still think it's a very interesting city, rich in Iowa history. Its mines produced lead for Civil War bullets. Its shipyards built boats that Mark Twain may have piloted. In frontier days Dubuque boasted of making plows "for all Christendom."

The Melleray Abbey is a good place to be a Trappist monk, if you want to be a Trappist monk. The vertical streets are wonderful if you're training to be a mountain climber. And the bluffs provide a panoramic view of the Mississippi, still fresh from Minnesota lakes, if you like to take pictures. But for spending a lifetime in Dubuque . . .

"Haven't you ever left the city?" I asked.

"Oh, I've been around," Albert replied, "I've played with a band."

"High school band?"

"Tommy Dorsey's band."

"You're kidding."

"I gave it up. Too much traveling. I've got a family, you know."

He invited me for Sunday dinner. While his wife was setting the table, he put Tommy Dorsey's "Lonesome Road" on the phonograph. "That's me," he said, "playing one of the clarinets."

I laughed. "Prove it."

He reached into a cabinet for a clarinet, put a new reed into the mouthpiece, and started the record all over again. Standing at the table, gently beating time with his foot, he began to play. He blended in perfectly with the music.

Loralee, his wife, stood listening. A gorgeous blonde, she had eyes that could enslave a man. Three children galloped into the dining room. Their noses were running.

I was glad I had the freedom to go to New York. I had a lot of living to do and many things to see.

Five years later, when I was working in Davenport, I obeyed an impulse to drive up and see Albert. He was still Linotyping at the newspaper. He invited me to have Christmas dinner with them. Loralee seemed lovelier than ever and the children didn't have running noses. I talked about my interesting experiences as a taxi driver in Havana and about meeting Robert Graves while I was trying to write a novel in Majorca. And Albert told me he had a better shift and was earning a few pennies more per hour.

After the coffee Albert told the kids that he could play almost as well as Bennie Goodman. Loralee handed him the clarinet and put a record on the hi-fi. I could hardly recognize Albert. A new, vibrant personality emerged from the dull shell of the Linotyper. I wanted to take him by the hand and lead him out of Dubuque. It was a shame that he was doomed to waste his life at the damn keyboard.

I dropped in on them a few years later. He was getting gray already and his wife's hair had more silver than gold. The children were grown. The two girls were anxious to get away from the dinner table because they had dates. The boy was complaining that his tire kept getting flat. When Albert reached for his clarinet, the kids hurried out of the house.

"Still playing?" I asked, trying to keep the sympathy out of my voice.

"Still at it," he said, shrugging.

I took a long look at Loralee. I wondered if she realized what her beauty had done to this man's life.

She put a record on the stereo and started a tape recorder. Albert picked up his clarinet.

"He likes to feel he's playing in a big band." she explained to me softly. "So he plays while the record is going. And we get it all down on tapes. Then we really have him playing with Artie Shaw . . . Glenn Miller . . . Woody Herman . . . all of them."

I felt sorry for Albert, accepting such a substitute when he could have had the real thing. Of course his wife was a lovely woman, but . . .

I was on my way to Seattle, where I wanted to saturate myself with the atmosphere of the Northwest. But I didn't like the fogs and so, after a few months, I went down to San Francisco, where I didn't like the traffic. Los Angeles was beginning to look like a slum and so after a few more months I went to Nevada to Linotype on the Las Vegas Sun, where the people were wonderful. But as more months went by I got tired of the desert and wanted to see the ocean again. San Diego was just another rat race of pushing tape into automated machines and so I went to Tijuana where I rented a room in a cheap hotel and began writing a lousy novel about a Mexican barmaid.

On the day before Christmas I looked out at the shabby streets of Tijuana and felt an uncontrollable urge to get back to the Midwest. Tijuana is no place to spend Christmas, nor is California, nor Texas, nor Florida with its paper icicles hanging from palm trees; no, not even New York, where Christmas has become a Broadway spectacular, produced by a Hollywood stage manager. The place to spend Christmas is in the Midwest, where the winding rivers lie frozen like diamond bracelets among ermine hills of pure white snow. I wanted to get back to Dubuque.

The connections were poor and it was past midnight when I was walking up the icy hill with a quart of good rum for Albert and a black silk mantilla for Loralee. With joyous lights shining from the windows, Dubuque was as beautiful as a Christmas card.

Loralee took my coat, asked me to sit down, and then sat across the room, beside the glistening tree. The tape was softly playing Guy Lombardo's holiday music.

"The children are gone," she said. "They have families of their own."

"Albert?" I asked.

186

"I thought you knew. He died a year ago. Just passed away in his sleep."

I noticed the tin round boxes of tapes.

"You've been playing his music?" I asked.

She put a Kleenex to her eyes. "It's him," she said, her voice breaking, "playing with all the big bands."

In the glow of the many-colored lights her skin seemed soft and youthful. In her maturity she was lovelier than ever.

I looked through the window at the snow-packed streets. They seemed desolate, like the desolate streets of every town, every city, every country, where a man is alone on Christmas. And I understood why Albert had been so contented in Dubuque. Here, in his home, was heaven enough.

Loralee reached for the glass of wine that was beside her.

"I've been lonesome," she said. "It's been more than a year."

I sipped my wine. "It's been a lifetime," I said.